User manual to S24 Ultra (5G)

MW00916169

A complete vital user guide with the most up-to-date Android tips and tricks for beginners and seniors to configure and setup Galaxy S24 Ultra Device.

Professor Liberty

Table of Contents

4

8

INTRODUCTION

The User Manual for the Samsung Galaxy S24 Ultra 5G is a dynamic guidebook that provides extensive support in maximizing the functionality of your device. It serves as a vital tool for individuals of all proficiency levels in the realm of mobile technology, tailored to equip you with the requisite understanding and proficiency to effectively navigate the device. This manual encompasses detailed guidance on every aspect and fitness of the Samsung Galaxy S24 Ultra 5G, accompanied by insightful pointers and techniques that may have eluded your awareness.

Chapter 1
Setting up device

Nano-SIM cards are used by your device. There might be a preinstalled SIM card, or it could be possible to make use of your old SIM card. The network indicators of the 5G service are dependent on your network availability and the specification of your service providers. For further information, speak with the service provider.

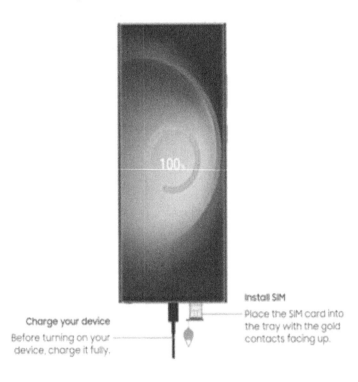

Install SIM

Place the SIM card into the tray with the gold contacts facing up.

Charge your device

Before turning on your device, charge it fully.

18

Note: This mobile device is rated IP68 for water and dust resistance. In order to preserve the dust-resistance/water-resistance features of this mobile device, you should ensure that your SIM card tray apertures are kept dry and clear of dirt, with the tray itself being securely fixed prior it becomes immersed in liquid.

Wireless power share

You can wirelessly charge any of your supported Samsung devices with the use your phone. Certain features will not be available while you share power.

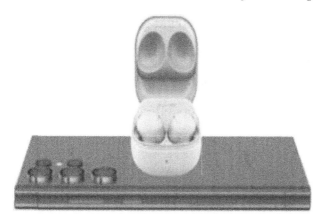

1.   Navigate to your Settings, you should tap on Battery & device care > then select Battery > then the Wireless powers sharing.

2.   Tap on Battery limit then you select a percentage. The wireless powers sharing will automatically turn off Once your device reach that charging level.

3.   Tap on to enable your charging feature.

4.   With your device face down, you should place the supported device at the top of the back your device to charge it. You will get a vibration or notification sound once charging begins.

Note: Most Qi-Certified gadgets are compatible with wireless powers sharing. needs a minimum of 30% of battery to be shared. Each device has a different speed for charge and power efficiency. Certain covers, accessories and other devices made by another manufacturer might not work. Take off each device's cover if you're having problems connecting or if charging is taking a long time.

For optimum results while you are using the Wireless powers sharing, take note:

- Before utilizing this feature, take off any covers or accessories. With respect to the type of cover or accessory, your wireless powers sharing might not function properly.

- Each device may have a different wireless charging coil location, so you might need to reposition it in order to establish a connection. A vibration or notification will sound as charging begins, letting you know when a connection has been made.

- The reception of your calls or data services can be impacted, depending upon your network's environment.

- The condition of your device and the surrounding environment can affect your efficiency or charging speed.

- Avoid using your headphones when you are charging via Wireless powers sharing.

Turning on device

Turn your smartphone on, press on your side key. If the device's body is fractured or cracked, avoid using it. Only use your device once it is fixed.

- ❖ Press & hold down your Side key to turn your device on.

- To turn your device off, you should press& hold down your Side/ Volume keys simultaneously, then you tap on ⏻ Power off. Once prompted confirm.

- To restart device, you should press & hold down your Side & Volume simultaneously then you tap on ↺ , Restart. Confirm once you are prompted.

TIP: Select ⚙ Advanced features > then Side key > How to turn off your phone, to get additional information about turning off your phone from Settings.

Note: The rear of your device's antennae must be free of obstructions for optimum 5G performance; check your service provider regarding network availability. A case or cover may also affect 5G performance.

Using Setup Wizard

The Setup Wizard walks you through the fundamentals of setting your device the very first time your device is turned on.

Kindly go through the prompts to pick a defaulting language, connect to a Wi-Fi® network and set up your accounts and also select location services, you can also learn about your device's functions, and many more.

1.   From your Settings, you should tap on Accounts & backup > then on Bring the data from the old devices.

2.   Adhere to the prompts then choose contents you want to transfer.

Locking/unlocking your device

You can utilize the lock screen features of your device to secure device. Your device automatically locks once your screen times run out by default.

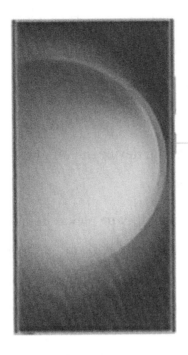

Side key
Press to lock.
Press to turn on the
screen, and then
swipe the screen to
unlock it.

The Side keys settings

Your Side key's assigned shortcuts are customizable.

Double pressing

Select the feature that will be launched once your Side
button is double pressed.

1.   From your Settings, tap on   Advanced
features > then Side key.

2.   Tap on Double-press to activate this feature,
then you tap on any option:

- Quick launch the camera (by default)
- Open the application.

Press & hold

Select the feature that will be launched once you press & hold your Side key.

1. From your Settings, you should tap on Advanced features > then Side key.

2. Under your Press & hold heading, you should tap on an option:

- Wake Bixby (by default)
- will Power off menu

Accounts

You can Set up your accounts and manage them.

TIP: Contacts, calendars, email, and various other features may be supported by accounts.

For further information, get in touch with the service provider.

Adding up Google Account

To get to the Google's Cloud Storages, installed apps, and to fully utilize your Android features on your smartphone, login onto your account on Google.

Google Devices Protections is enabled once you setup lock screen and sign into your Google account. Resetting to your factory settings requires the information associated with your Google Account.

1.   From your Settings, you should tap on 🔄 Accounts & backup > then Manage accounts.

2.   Tap on ➕ Add account > then Google.

Adding Samsung account

You should sign into Samsung account if you want to get access to exclusive contents and to fully utilize your Samsung applications.

❖ From your Settings, you should tap on Samsung account.

Adding an Outlook account

To access and manage your email messages, login to your own Outlook® account.

1.   From your Settings, tap on 🔄 Accounts & backup > then on Manage accounts.

2.   Tap on Add account > then Outlook.

Setting up your voicemail

You can configure the voicemail service once you get in for the very first time. Using your phone's app, you may access voicemail. Options could differ depending on the service provider.

1.   From your ⓒ Phone, you should touch & hold on your 1 key or you tap on 👀 Voicemail.

2.   Adhere to the tutorial so as to make your password, you can record a greeting, then you record your name.

Navigation bar

You can use the full-screen gestures or the navigation keys to navigate your smartphone.

Recent apps

Home

Back

The Navigation buttons

You can utilize buttons along your bottom screen for a quick navigation.

1.   From your Settings, you should tap on
Display > then Navigation bar > then select Buttons.

2.   Tap on an option under the Buttons orders to
select the side of your screen your Back with your
Recent applications icons display.

Navigation gestures

To have a completely free screen, you can hide the
bottom-of-your-screen navigation buttons. To
navigate your device, swipe instead.

1.   From your Settings, tap on   Display > then
select Navigation bar > then Swipes gestures to
activate the feature.

2.   Tap on any option for customization:

- More options: Lets you select any gesture type
  with the sensitivity.

- Gesture hint: This shows lines at your bottom
  screen where all screen gesture is found.

- ❖ Switch applications when hints hidden: Once
  your gesture hint goes off, you may still be able
  to switch between applications employing the
  gesture if the option is activated.

❖ Showing buttons to hide keyboards: Display an icon in your screen right bottom corner to hide your keyboard once your device is on portrait mode.

❖ Block S Pen gestures: (Only compatible with the Galaxy S24 Ultra) Stops S Pens from creating navigation gestures.

Customizing home screen

Your device's Home screen serves as the initial point of navigation. In addition to adding more Home screens, deleting screens, rearranging screens, and selecting a primary Home screen, you may arrange your favorite applications & widgets here.

App icons

You should use your application icons to open an application from any of your Home screen.

❖ From your Apps, you should touch & hold down any application icon, then you tap on ⊕ Adds to Home.

To remove any icon

❖ From any of your Home screen, you should touch & hold down an application icon, then you tap on ⬚ Remove.

Note: Removing any icon from your Home screen doesn't delete such application, it only removes such icon from that Home screen.

Wallpaper

You can change the appearance of your Lock and Home screen, by selecting any of your favorite photos, preinstalled wallpaper, or videos.

1. Press and hold your screen from any of your Home screen, then select ⬚ Wallpaper & style.

2. To access your various available wallpapers, tap on any of the choices below:

- Tap on your Lock screen, then your Home screen photos for editing them.

- Change wallpapers: Select from a selection of wallpaper options, you can as well download additional ones from your Galaxy Themes.

- Color palette: Based on the colors on your wallpaper select a palette.
- Dim wallpaper once Dark modes is on: Activate to apply the Dark mode on your wallpaper.

Themes

Prepare a theme that you want to apply on your Home & Lock screens, app icons and wallpapers.

1. From any of your Home screens, you should touch & hold down the screen.

2. Tap on 🖌 Themes, then you tap any theme for previewing & downloading it.

3. Tap on ☰ Menu > then tap My stuff > then on Themes to view your downloaded themes.

4. Tap any theme, then you tap Apply, in order to apply your chosen theme.

Icons

You can apply a different icon tab to replace your default icons.

1. From any of your Home screens, you should press and hold down screen.

2.	Tap on 🖌 Themes > then tap Icons, then you tap an icon set, for preview & download it.

3.	Tap on ☰ Menu > then tap My stuff > then Icons in order to view your downloaded icons.

4.	Tap any icon, then you tap Apply so as to apply your chosen icon set.

Your Widgets

To provide fast access to information or applications, add up widgets to the home screens.

1.	From your Home screen, you should touch & hold your screen.

2.	Tap on ⬚ Widgets then you tap any widget setup to access it.

3.	To add any widget that you want to your home screen, swipe over it and then tap Add.

Customizing your Widgets

Whenever you are done adding a widget, you can always customize how your widget function or where you want it to be located on your Home screen.

❖ From your Home screen, you should hold down any widget, then you tap any option:

- ⊞ Create stack: This Add any widgets of similar size to be stack on the same location on your screen.

- 🗑 Remove: This will delete any widget on your screen.

- ⚙ Settings: This helps you to customize the appearance and function of your widget.

- ⓘ App info: Review your widget usage, the permissions, and even more.

Setting up your Home screen

You can personalize Home screens and your Applications screens.

1. From any of your Home screen, you should touch & hold down screen.

2. Tap on ⚙ Settings then customize:

- Home screens layouts: Configure your smartphone to have distinct home and

34

applications screens, or to have a single home screen that stores all of your applications are found.

- Home screens grid: Select any layout to define the arrangement of your icons on your Home screen.

- Applications screens grid: Select any layout to define the arrangement of your icons on your Apps screen.

- Folder grid: Select any layout to define how your folders will be arranged.

- Add up media pages to Homes screen: When activated, to view a media page, you should swipe right on your home screen. Tap to see the media services that are available.

- Show Applications screens buttons in Home screens: To make accessing the Apps screen easier, this add up a button to your Home screen.

- Locks Home screens layouts: This helps Keep items from being moved or removed from your Home screen.

- Adds new applications to Homes screen: Installed apps will be automatically added to your Home screen.

- Hides applications on Home & Apps screens: Select which apps to hide off your Home & App screens. In order to retrieve the hidden apps, go to this particular screen. Finder searches may yield results for hidden applications, which remain installed.

- Application icon badges: Turn on to display badge on applications that have active notifications. Additionally, you may select the badge's design.

- Swipes down for the notifications panel: If you activate this feature, you can swipe down from anywhere on your home screen to open your notification panel.

- Rotate to landscape mode: This automatically rotate your home screen whenever your device switches from portrait to the landscape mode.

- Abouts Home screens: Check out the version information.

- Contact us: You can contact your Samsung support from a Samsung Members.

Easy mode

With your Easy mode layouts, you get larger icons and texts which makes it much simpler for visual experience. You change your screen layout from the default to a much simpler layout.

1. From your Settings, tap on

Tue, January 17

12:45 PM

Tap for weather info

Internet   Gallery   Camera

Phone   Messages   Apps

Apps list

2. Tap on to activate this feature. These below options appear:

- Touch & hold delay: You can configure how long does it takes to identify a continuous touch as touch & hold.

- Highly contrast keyboards: let you pick keyboard with a high contrast color.

38

The Status bars

Status bar gives you your device notification alerts by the left side, and your information by your right.

Status icons

Battery full	Charging	Mute	Vibrate
Airplane mode	Bluetooth active	Location active	Alarm

Notification icons

Missed calls	Call in progress	New message	Voicemail
New email	Download	Upload	App update

TIP: From the Quick settings menu, select More options > then the Status bar to set up settings for the notification of your Status bar.

Notification panel

To have instant access to settings, notifications, and more, just launch your Notification panel.

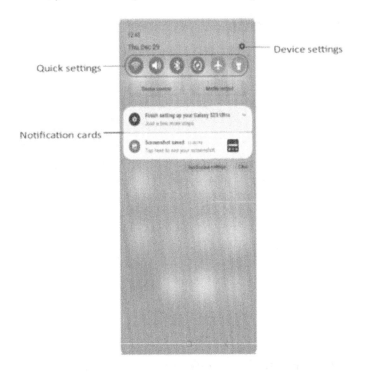

Viewing your Notification panel

You can always access your Notification panel at any of your screen.

1.   Simply Swipe downward on your screen to reveal your Notification panel.

  • To open any item, you should tap on it.

- Drag on any notification you want to clear right or left to clear only it.

- To clear every of your notifications, you should tap Clear.

- To customize your notifications, you should tap your Notification settings.

2.   From your bottom screen drag up or tap on ⟨ to close your Notification panel.

The Quick settings

Using your Quick settings, your Notification panel offers instant access to your device operations. The most popular Quick setting; settings are displayed by those icons below. As an icon is enabled or disabled, its color changes. There can be more settings available on your device.

1.   Drag down your Status bar to display your Notification panel.

2.   You then again downward from top of your screen to reveal your Quick settings.

- Turn off or on your quick settings icons by tapping on it.

41

- Open your quick settings icons setting by tapping & holding them down.

| Wi-Fi | Sound | Bluetooth | Auto rotate |
| Airplane mode | Location | Power saving | Dark mode |

Your Quick setting selections

These below options are available in your Quick settings.

- Finder search: This help Search your device.

- Power off: Provides Power off & your Restart options.

- Pen settings: Shortcut to your device settings menu.

- More options: This helps reorder your Quick settings and also changes the layout of your button.

- Device control: This controls any other device whenever a supported application such as the Google Home or SmartThings installed.

- Media output: this access your Media panel, controls the playback of videos and audio that are connected.

- Brightness slider: When dragged, it helps you to adjust your screen brightness.

The S Pen

There are numerous useful functions offered by your S Pen. To open applications, drawing pictures, or taking notes, employ your S Pen. Certain S Pen features, such tapping your touchscreen (exclusive to the Galaxy S24 Ultra), may not function if your smartphone is close to a magnet.

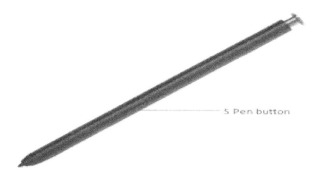
S Pen button

Removing your S Pen

S Pen is stored at bottom on your device for easy access. In order to use your S Pen for any remote functions, your device also charges it.

❖ Push on your S Pen inwardly in order to release, then you slip it out.

Note: Make sure your S Pen slot & opening are maintained dry and free of debris, and that the pen is firmly inserted prior to exposing your device to liquids in order to preserve its water- and dust-resistance features.

Air view

Hover your S Pen on your screen in order to look up information about any on your or preview your content. These are the available Air viewing features:

• Previewing an email prior to opening it.

• Previewing the contents for photo album/ enlarge picture.

• Previewing videos & navigate towards specific scenes via hovering over your timeline.

• Viewing name/description of any icon/ button.

Note: Your preview functions are only available whenever the on-screen pointer of your S Pen's are solid colors.

Air Actions

Using your S Pen, you may set up shortcuts to your favorite applications, complete actions, navigate on screens of your devices and more. You can also utilize the button and gestures or movements of your S pen to conduct remote functions.

Only S Pens having Bluetooth Low Energy, or BLE, that have been approved by Samsung can use S Pen remote capability. Your S Pen will disconnect from any device if it is too far away or when there's interference. For Air operations to function, your S Pen needs to be connected.

❖ From your Settings, tap on Advanced features > then select S Pen > then Air action for activating this feature.

Holding your S Pen buttons shortcuts

You can set up shortcut if you press & hold down your S Pen button. This option has been set to open your Camera application by default.

1.   From your Settings, you should tap on Advanced features > then S Pen > then select Air actions.

2.   Tap on Press & hold Pen button, then you tap on ⬤ to activate the feature.

Anywhere actions

Holding your S Pen button while doing one of these gestures will allow you to access configurable shortcuts called Anywhere actions: down, up, right, left, or shake. These include apps, S Pen features, and navigation that are accessible from any of your screen.

⌇ Back Left to right

⤺ Recents Right to left

⤊ Home Up and down

⤵ Smart select Down and up

≋ Screen write Zigzag

1.   From your Settings, tap on ⬤ Advanced features > then select S Pen > the Air actions.

2.   Tap on any Gesture icon that is under the Anywhere actions for customizing your shortcut.

App actions

Your S Pen can be utilized for specific actions on certain applications.

1.   From your Settings, tap on ⬤ Advanced features > then select S Pen > then Air actions.

2.   Tap on any application to view available shortcuts.

3.   Tap on to activate your shortcuts when you are making use of that app.

General application actions

When utilizing camera or media applications that aren't included in your application action list, you could customize a few general actions.

1.   From your Settings, tap on Advanced features > then on S Pen > then Air actions.

2.   Under the General application actions, you should tap on any action for change.

The Screens off memos

You could write a memo with your screen turned off. You must activate the setting your screen off memo.

1.   Detach your S Pen when your screen is still off, then you write on your screen.

2.   Tap on an option for customizing your memo:

- Color: Allows you change your pen color.

- Pen settings: Tap to make use of your pen tool. Then you tap on again to adjust your line thickness.

- ⬦Eraser: Tap on to employ your eraser tool. Tap on once more to erase all.

3.   Tap on Save to let you save your memos into your Samsung Notes application.

TIP: If your S Pen has been removed already from your device, you should press on your S Pen button, then you tap on your screen to begin a note even while your screen stays off.

Pinning to your Always On Displays

A note that is on your Always On Displays can be edited or pinned.

1.   Tap on ⬦ Pinned to Always on Displays in the screen-off memos.

2.   Tap on Pinned to the Always On Displays.

Air commands

Use the familiar S Pen's features, such as Samsung Notes, Screen Write, and Smart Select, from any of your screen.

Settings

1.　　Tap on ⬤ Air commands or you hold your S Pen near to your screen, in order to make your pointer appear, then you press on your S Pen's button once.

2.　　You can tap on any option:

- ⊕ Create note: Lets you open a fresh note in your Samsung Notes application.

- Viewing all notes: Lets you open your Samsung Notes application and allows you view a list of all the notes you have made.

- Smart select: Helps draw around a section of your screen to be collected in your Gallery application.

- Screen write: Helps you capture screenshots & draw or write on them.

- Live messages: Lets you Use your S Pen to write or create a brief animated message.

- AR Doodle: Use your AR camera function for drawing interactive doodles.

- Translate: Move your S Pen pointer across a word to see how it is translated into a different language and hear its pronunciation.

- PENUP: Uses your S Pen for coloring, drawing, editing, and for sharing your live drawings.

- ⊕Add: Add to your Air commands menu's list of applications and functions.

- ⚙Settings: You can modify Air Command's appearance and functionality as well as the applications and functions that it offers.

Creating note

You can open a fresh note directly from your Samsung Notes application.

❖ Tap on 🖉 Air command >then you select ⊞ Create note.

Viewing all notes

To see a list of the notes you've created, open your Samsung Notes application.

❖ Tap on 🖉 Air command > then select 🗐 to View all note.

Smart selects

Smart select is a feature which let you copy contents from your screens, which can then be added into your Gallery application or to share among your contact list.

1.   Tap on ✏ Air command > then select 🌀 Smart select.

2.   Tap on any shape from your menu, then you drag your S Pen to choose your content. These below options appear:

- ✏ Pin/Insert: Helps you add shortcut to your obtained content in an application or place it on any of your Home screen.

- 🔲 Auto select: Give Smart Select permission to choose content to be extracted automatically.

- ✏ Draw: Allows you to draw on your captured content.

- Ⓣ Extract text: Locate and take extract text out of your chosen content.

- ⮜ Share: Select a sharing option for sharing your contents to others.

- ⬇ Tap on Save.

TIP: You may tap on [GIF] Animation for recording animation or you Pin to your screen to help pin your content the screen utilizing your Smart select.

Screen write

With your Screen write, you can capture screenshots then draw or write on them.

1. Tap on 🖊 Air command > then select 🔺 Screen write.

2. Then your current screen will be captured, then pen tool will appear. You are provided with these editing tools:

- Crop: You should drag on the edges of your screen to crop your captured contents.

- ✒ Pen type: Let you draw on your screenshot. You should tap on your Pen icon again to change your pen tip, color, and size.

- ◇ Eraser: Help you erase drawings or writing on your screenshot.

- ⬑ Undo: Helps you revert your previous action.

- ⬏ Redo: Helps you repeat your previous action which was reversed.

- ⬈ Share: Select a sharing option for sharing your content to others.

- ⬚ Scroll capture: Helps you capture any of those scrollable section of your screen that might be concealed.

- ⬇ Tap on Save. Your content will be saved to your Gallery application.

TIP: You should hold on your S Pen's button for erasing your drawings in your screen memo.

Live messages

The live messages help you record a written message or animated drawings.

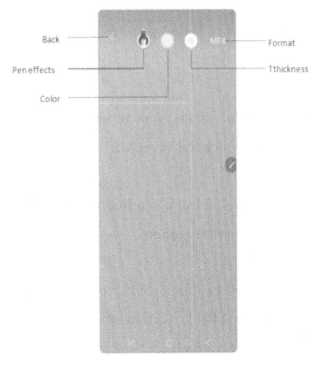

Back — Format

Pen effects — Tthickness

Color

1.   Tap on 🖊 Air command > then select 💚 Live messages.

2.   Choose any of these background options:

- Collection: You can view all the live messages that you've created.

- Gallery: Let you pick any video or image for your background.

- Camera: Help you capture images used for your background.

- Color: Select a background color.

3. You should follow the directions to start creating live message.

4. Tap on Done then save.

AR Doodle

Use augmented reality to create interactive doodles on faces and other items that are viewable through your camera's lens.

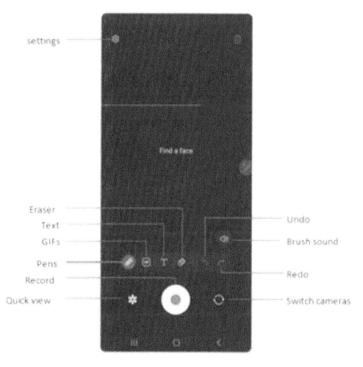

1.	Tap on 🖊 Air command > then select 🖊 AR Doodle.

2.	You should choose between your rear or front cameras as you tap on ⚙ Switch cameras.

3.	Place your camera properly so your target will be centered in your screen.

4.	Use your S Pen to make a drawing of a doodle.

- Your doodle tracks your face's movements at real time.

5.	Tap on ⊙ Record for saving any video of AR Doodle.

Translate

Use your S Pen for translating words and hear their pronunciation as you hover above them.

1.	Tap on 🖊 Air command > then select 🄰 Translate.

2.	Tap on ▤ your icon to switch between translating phrases & translating words:

- Phrases: This helps in translating entire phrases.

- Words: Helps in translating words.

3. Tap on ⊤ your source & your target languages to transform them to your desired languages.

4. You should hover your S Pen across a word.

- Tap on 🔊 Sound for hearing the pronunciation of word from your source language.

. Tap on 📋 Copy, so you can save your selected texts along with translation to clipboard.

5. Tap on ✕ Close for closing Translate.

PENUP

You can utilize your S pen to edit, draw, color and even for sharing live drawings.

- ❖ Tap on ● Air command > then select ◯ PENUP.

Adding shortcuts

Make changes and customization to your Air commands menu via the addition of shortcuts to applications & functions.

1. Tap on ⊘ Air command > then select ⊕ Add.

2. Tap on the functions or applications you would like to add to the Air command menu.

- To remove any application shortcut, you should tap on ⊖ Remove.

3. Tap on ⟨ then Navigate upward to save the selection.

Setting your Air Command

Quickly access apps and S Pen features in a convenience and collapsible menu that you can drag anywhere on the screen.

- ❖ From your Settings, you should tap on ◯ Advanced features > then select S Pen > then Air command to set up these settings:

- Menu styles: Select how you want your Air commands menu to display once it is opened.

- Shortcuts: Select the shortcuts which are offered on Air command.

- Shows Air commands icons: Helps show icon for your Air commands menu.

- Open Air commands with the Pens button: Utilizes your S Pen buttons to access your Air commands menu.

Configuring your S Pen settings

Settings for the S Pen can be modified. Options vary by service provider.

- ❖ From your Settings, you should tap on Advanced features > then select S Pen for setting up these subsequent settings:

- Air actions: Set up how your remote control works while you are using applications.

- Air commands: Customize your Air command menu's appearance, behavior, and shortcuts.

- Air view: Turn on or off Air View.

- S Pen for texting: To write on address bars, search fields, and other text areas, with your S Pen. The S Pen allows you to alter the text that has been converted from your handwriting.

- When the S Pen 's is removed: Select the outcome that occurs when removing your S

Pen. Select either Create note, Open Air command, or Do Nothing.

- Screens off memo: To create a screen off memo, detach your S Pen and write on your screen while it is off. Your screen-off memo is stored in your Samsung Notes.

- Quick notes: To begin a fresh note, you should press & hold down your S Pen button, then you tap on your screen twice using your S Pen.

- More S-Pen's settings: Set up your S Pen's various behaviors, such as sounds, vibrations, and connections.

- About the S Pen: Check out the features of your S Pen version details.

- contact us: Use Samsung Members to get in touch with the Samsung support.

Bixby

Bixby, which is an AI virtual assistant which learns, develops, and as well adapts with you. It integrates with your favorite applications, learns your patterns, and assists you in setting up reminders depending on time and place.

❖ From any of your Home screen, you should press & hold your Side key.

TIP: From your Apps list, you may access the Bixby.

Bixby Vision

Bixby works together with your Gallery, Camera, & Internet applications to provide you an in-depth comprehension of the things you see. It offers contextual icons use for shopping, QR code scanning, landmark identification, and translation.

Camera

Your camera's viewfinder offers Bixby Vision to help you make sense of all that you see.

❖ From your 📷 Camera, you should tap on More > then select Bixby Visions then follow the direction.

Gallery

You can employ your Bixby Vision on images and pictures saved on your Gallery application.

1. From your ✽ Gallery, you should tap on any picture for view.

2. Tap on 👁 Bixby Vision then you follow the instructions.

Internet

You can use Bixby Vision to learn more regarding an image that appears in your Internet application.

1.   From your ⬤ Internet, you should touch & hold down any image until you see a pop-ups menu appear.

2.   Tap on Search using Bixby Vision then you follow the directions.

Modes & Routines

Configure your modes & routines to have your device adjust its settings automatically based on what you're doing or where you are.

❖ From your Settings, you should tap on ⬤ Modes & Routines for these pages:

- Modes: Helps select a mode that is dependent on the things you are doing or where you are.

- Routines: Helps you create routines that are dependent on place or time.

Digital wellbeing & the parental controls

Receiving a daily overview of how much you use your applications, the amount number of notifications that you receive, with just how regularly you check your mobile device can help you monitor and control the digital habits of yours. Additionally, you can set up your device to assist you in unwinding before bed.

❖ From your Settings, tap on Digital Wellbeing & parental controls for these features:

• Tap on your Dashboard to check out these:

❖ Screen time: Helps you see the duration of each day's opening and usage of an app.

❖ Notifications received: Lets you check the number of notifications that an application has sent you each day.

❖ Times opened/Unlocked: See how frequently an application has been used in a given day.

• Screens time goals: Establish a target for your screen time and monitor the daily average.

- App timers: Assign a daily timeout to each application's use.

- Driving monitor: Track the applications that you use most frequently by using your vehicle's Bluetooth to track how much time you spend on screens.

- Volume monitor: Select an audio source so you can keep an eye on your volume and protect your hearing from damage.

- Parental controls: Use Google's Family Link application to keep an eye on your kids' online activities. You have the ability to select apps, apply content controls, set up a limit to screen time and monitor screen time.

Always On Display

With Always On Displays (AOD), you can see message alerts and missed calls, as well as your date and time and other personalized information, without having to unlock your device.

1.   From your Settings, tap on 🔒 Lock screen > then select Always On Displays.

2.   Tap on ⬤ to activate this feature, then you set these below options:

- Select when to display notifications and a clock on your device when it isn't in use.

- Clock style: Modify the color and style of your clock in the Always on Displays & Lock screen.

- Shows music information: Display your music details while your FaceWidgets music's controllers is actively in use.

- Screen orientations: Choose between portrait & landscape mode for the AOD.

- Auto brightness: Always On Display's brightness can be modified automatically.

- About the Always On Displays: Check the license details and software version that is currently installed.

AOD themes

You always apply a customize themes as your Always On Displays.

1.	From any of your Home screen, you should touch & hold down your screen, then you tap on Themes > then AODs.

- Tap on a AOD for previewing & downloading it into the My Always On Displays.

2.	Tap on ⊟ Menu > then select My stuff > then AODs to view your downloaded themes.

3.	Tap on an AOD, then you tap on Apply to apply.

Biometric security

You can utilize your biometrics, to help you secure, and unlock device, even also to login to an account of yours, or any sensitive application of yours.

Facial recognition

For unlocking your screen, turn on your facial recognition. You need to set up a PIN, pattern, or password in order to be able to use your face unlock your smartphone.

- Compared to passwords, PINs, and patterns, your face recognition remains less secure. Someone or anything that resembles you could unlock your device.

- Certain conditions, such as wearing glasses, beards, hats, or excessive makeup, may impair face recognition.

- Make sure your camera's lens remains clean and you're within an area with good lighting before registering your face.

1.   From your Settings, tap on ⬤ Security & privacy > then select Biometrics > before Face recognition.

2.   Follow the directions to register face.

Facial recognition management

Customize how you want your face recognition to work.

- ❖ From your Settings, tap on ⬤ Security & privacy > then select Biometrics > then Face recognition.

- Remove faces data: This deletes already existing faces.

- Face unlocks: You activate or deactivate your facial recognition and security.

- Stay on Locks screens until swipe: After you unlock the device using your face recognition, stay on your Lock screen till you swipe your screen.

- Brighten screen: This helps increase the brightness of your screen temporarily to help recognize your face in dark surroundings.

- About faces recognitions: find out more info on securing device, using your facial recognition.

Your Fingerprints scanner

In specific applications, you can use your fingerprint recognition instead of typing passwords.

Additionally, when entering into your account on Samsung, you may employ fingerprints to confirm your identity. You need to set a PIN, password, or pattern before you may unlock your smartphone using your fingerprint.

1.   From your Settings, tap on ⬤ Security & privacy > the Biometrics > then click Fingerprints.

2.   Follow the directions to register fingerprint.

Managing your Fingerprint

You can Add up, delete, and even rename your fingerprints.

- ❖ From your Settings, tap on ⬤ Security & privacy > then select Biometrics > then Fingerprints for the subsequent options:

- Add fingerprints: You should just follow the direction of the prompts on your device to register additional fingerprints.

- Checks added fingerprints: This Scans the fingerprint to check if already is been registered.

Verification settings of Fingerprint

When using supported applications and actions, employ fingerprint recognition for verifying your identity.

- ❖ From your Settings, tap on ⬤ Security & privacy > then select Biometrics > then Fingerprints.

- Fingerprints unlocks: Employs the use of your fingerprint to identify whenever you're unlocking device.

- Fingerprints always on: This helps scans fingerprint even if your screen is turned off.

- Use to signs into websites: Uses fingerprints for signing in on websites.

- Uses for Samsungs accounts verifications: Instead of using your Samsung account's passwords for verifying yourself, you can employ your fingerprints.

Biometrics settings

Set up your choices for security features using biometrics.

- ❖ From your Settings, tap on ⬤ Security & privacy > then select Biometrics for these options:

- Shows unlocks transitions effects: Display transition effects, once you employ the use of your biometrics for unlocking your device.

- Abouts unlocking via the biometrics: Find out more info on using the biometrics for securing your phone.

Multi window

You can Multitask by utilizing many applications simultaneously. Applications which support the Multi window™ could be seen together displayed in split screen. You may swap between your applications and make adjustment to their sizes and windows.

Split screen control

1.   From any of your screen, you should tap on|||
Recent apps.

2.   Tap on your app icon, then you tap on Open in splits screen view.

3.   Tap on any application in your other window in order to include it to your split screen views.

- Drag on middle of your windows border for adjustment of your window size.

Window controls

Automatically the Window controls change the way application windows are showed in split screen view.

1.   To resize your windows, you should drag your window border on the middle.

2.   Tap on your window border middle for these options:

- ↑↓ Switch window: This lets you swap between both windows.

- ☆ Add apps pair to: Let you create, add up an application pairs shortcuts into your Apps panel at your Edge screens.

The Edge panels

Edge panels consist of different kinds panels which are customizable, which could be easily accessed from your screen edge. Edge panels may be used for accessing applications, contacts, and tasks, even for viewing news, sports, with other information also.

❖ From your Settings, tap on 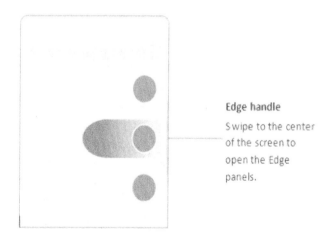 Display > then Edge panels, tap on ➤ to activate this feature.

Edge handle
Swipe to the center of the screen to open the Edge panels.

The Apps panel

One can always add applications to your Apps panels.

1.   From any of your screen, you should drag on Edge handle towards center of your screen. Then swipe till your Apps panel appears.

2.   Tap on an application or application pair shortcuts to launch it. You may also tap on ⋮⋮⋮ All apps to get a full application list.

- Drag your application icon from your Apps panel onto your open screen to open extra windows on the pop-up view.

To set up Apps panel

1.   Drag your Edge handle towards your screen's center from any of your screen. Swipe till your Apps panel is revealed.

2.   Tap on ✎ the Edit to include more applications to your Apps panel.

- To add up any application to your Apps panel, locate it from your screens left side, then tap on it for adding it to available space, found on right column.

- for creating folder shortcuts, you should drag any application from your left side screen at the top of any application from the columns by the right.

- Drag and drop each application to reposition them in your panel, in order to change their order to what you want.

- To remove any application, tap on ⁻ the Remove.

3.   Tap on ‹ Back to save your changes.

Set up Edge panel

You could always customize your Edge panels.

1.   From your Settings, tap on ⚙ Display > then on Edge panels > then Panels.

2.   There are the following choices:

- ✓ Checkbox: This disable or enable each panel.

- Edit (when available): This configures each individual panels.

- ⌕ Search: Search for panels which are either available for installation or installed.

- ⋮ More option:

  ❖ Reorders: This changes order to which your panels are arranged via dragging them towards the right or the left.

  ❖ Uninstall: This removes Edge panel downloaded on your device.

  ❖ Hides on Locks screens: Selects the panels to be hidden on your Lock screen whenever you set secure screens lock.

  - Galaxy Store: This helps to search for downloaded Edge panels, also even to download more from your Galaxy Store.

3. You should tap on ⟨ Back to save your changes.

The Edge panels style & position
You may change your position of your Edge handle.

  ❖ From your Settings, tap on ⚙ Display > then Edge panels > then Handle for the subsequent options:

- ⌃⌄ Edge handle: You can drag your Edge handle along your screen's edge to adjust its position.

- Position: Select either the Left or Right to set where your Edge screen will display on.

- Lock handles positions: When enabled, it helps prevent your handles positions from moving once it is touched & held.

- Style: Selects colors for your Edge handle.

- Transparency: To change your Edge handle's transparency, this drags your slider.

- Size: To change your Edge handle's size, drag your slider.

- Width: To modify Edge handle's width, drag your slider.

- Vibrate once handle gets touched: Your Edge handle will vibrate when it is touched.

About your Edge panel

You may see the software version that is currently installed and license details from your Edge panels feature's.

- From your Settings, tap on  Display > then select Edge panels > then Abouts Edge panels.

Entering text

Your text may be entered with your keyboard or by using your voice.

Toolbar

Quick access to your keyboard features is provided by the toolbar. Options differ depending on the service provider.

❖ On your Samsung keyboard, you should tap on ••• to Expand your toolbar for these options:

- ☺ Expression: Explore many emoji kinds, GIFs, create unique mixed emojis, and many more.

- Clipboard: To access your clipboard

- One-handed keyboard: Switches to the one-handed use layout.

- Voice input: Utilizes your Samsung voices inputs

- ⚙ Settings: Accesses your keyboard's settings.

- Handwriting: Let you utilize your handwriting for entering text (only in Galaxy S24 Ultra).

- ⌨ Split keyboard: This changes your keyboard into the split version which is separated.

- ⌨ Floating keyboards: This changes your keyboard into the version that floats, and could be moved to any place on your device screen.

- 🔍 Search: This finds specific phrases or words from your conversations.

- 🔤 Translate: Enters sentences or words on your keyboard for translating into other languages

- ⓣ Extract text: Allows you to extract and Identify text from your selected contents.

- 🔒 Samsung Pass: Allows you to make use of biometrics for fast, and secured entrance to your private data, with your online accounts.

- ⓖ Grammarly: This gives you suggestions from your Grammarly when you are typing.

- Emojis: Helps you insert emojis.

- GIFs: Add up animated GIFs.

- Bitmoji: Helps create your personalized emoji, then let you use it as stickers.

- Mojitok: This creates your personal stickers or let you automatically insert suggested stickers.

- AR Emoji: Helps create your personalized emoji then uses it as a sticker you may choose from.

- Spotify: Helps you add more music from your Spotify™.

- YouTube: Let you add up videos from the YouTube.

- Keyboard sizes: Allows you to adjust your keyboard width and height.

- Text editing: This Uses an editing panel which helps you to pinpoint the text which you wish to copy, & paste, or cut.

Setting up your Samsung keyboard

Customize your Samsung keyboard's settings. Options differs by your service provider.

- ❖ From your Samsung keyboard, you should tap on ⚙️ the Settings for these options:

  - Languages & types: Setup your keyboard type, then you select the languages which are accessible on your keyboard.

  - For switching between languages, you can swipe your space bar to the right or left.

The Smart typing

- Predictive texts: While you type, see recommended phrases and words.

- Suggest Emoji: When utilizing predictive text, add emojis.

- Suggests a sticker while typing: Look at suggested stickers as you type.

- Auto replace: This feature substitutes suggested text for what you input automatically.

- Suggests texts corrections: Highlight misspelled words with red and offer correction suggestions.

- Texts shortcuts: Make shortcuts for words and phrases that you use often.

- More typing option: Helps customize extra typing options.

Styles & layouts

- Keyboard toolbars: This reveals or conceal your keyboard toolbar.

- High contrast keyboards: Helps adjust and alter the size and color of your Samsung keyboard, to enhance contrast between your keys & background.

- Themes: Lets you select any theme you want for the keyboard.

- Mode: Lets you select between your landscape and portrait mode.

- Sizes & transparency: Provide you room for adjecting the transparency and size of your keyboard.

- Layout: This displays the numbers with unique characters on your keyboard.

- Fonts sizes: You should drag on your slider to regulate your font size.

- Custom symbols: Allow you change your symbol shortcuts in your keyboard.

More setting

- Voice inputs: Setups your voice input settings and services.

- Swipes, touch, & feedbacks: This Customizes your gestures & feedback.

- Handwriting: Helps you customize your handwriting options (only available in Galaxy S24 Ultra).

- S Pen for texts: This utilizes your S Pen for writing in your address bars, search fields, and any other text sections. Let you convert your handwriting to text, which you can also edit this converted text by using your S Pen (Available only in Galaxy S24 Ultra).

- Saves screenshots to the clipboards: lets you save screenshots to your keyboard clipboard.

- Selects third-party contents to uses: Permits the third-party keyboards feature.

- Resets to defaults settings: Allows you to return to your original keyboard settings, and wipes away all personalized data.

- Abouts Samsungs keyboards: Let you see version and all legal info about your Samsung's keyboard.

- Contact us: Helps you contact the Samsung support team via a Samsung Member.

Using your Samsungs voices inputs

You can speak what you want to text rather than typing.

❖ From your Samsung keyboard, you should tap on Voice input then you speak what you want to text.

Return to keyboard —————

Chapter 2

The Camera & Gallery

With your Camera application high-quality images and videos can be captured. You can see and edit pictures and videos that are stored on your Gallery.

Camera

Relish a full set of pro-grade video modes, with pro lenses and settings.

❖ From your Apps, tap on  the Camera.

TIP: You can easily double press your Side key, to launch your Camera app.

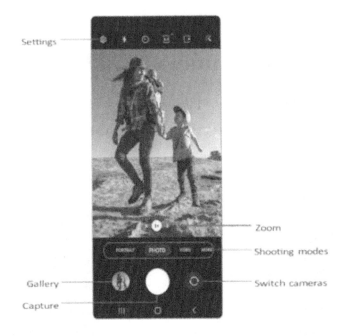

Settings

Zoom

Shooting modes

Gallery

Switch cameras

Capture

Navigate through your camera screen

Capture spectacular photos with your rear and front camera of your device.

1. From your Camera, you can prepare your shot using these below features:

    - Tap on your screen at the spot you want your camera focus.

❖ Once you tap on your screen, brightness scale displays. Drag on your slider for adjusting your brightness.

• For fast switch between your rear and front cameras, swipe your screen upwards or downwards.

• For zooming at a particular level, tap on the 1x & tap any option from bottom of your screen. (This is only available if you are using your rear camera.)

• When you wish to use another shooting mode, you can swipe your screen to the right/left.

To modify your camera settings, you should tap on ⚙ Settings.

Setting your shooting mode

This lets you select from the various shooting modes and let your camera to find the best mode for your shots.

❖ From your Camera, you can swipe your screen towards the left or right to change your shooting modes.

- Portrait: This helps you adject background of your photos to portrait photos.

- Photo: lets your camera find the best settings for your pictures.

- Video: lets your camera find the best settings for your videos.

- More: Helps you select other shooting modes available. Tap on ⊕ to Add and drag modes out or into your shootings modes trays which is on the bottom screen of your Camera.

- Expert RAW: Helps download your Expert RAWs mode of shooting.

❖ Pro: Lets you manually adjust your ISO sensitivity, white balance, exposure value, and color tone even when taking pictures.

❖ Pro video: This let you manually adjust your ISO sensitivity, white balance, exposure value, & even your color tone when you are recording videos.

❖ Single take: Helps you capture numerous photos and videos from multiple angles.

❖ Panorama: Let you create linear images by capturing photos in horizontal or even vertical direction.

❖ Night: Lets you capture pictures in low-light situations, with no use of your flash.

❖ Food: Captures pictures which brings out vivid colors of any food.

❖ Supers slow-mo: Helps you record videos with incredibly high rate of frames to view in on high quality in slow-mo. After a video is recorded, you can replay a certain portion of it in slow-mo.

❖ Slow motion: This helps one record videos at high frames rated to view on slow motion.

❖ Hyperlapse: Lets you create video with time lapse by recording with different frame rate. Your frame rate could be adjected, but it all depends on the scene which are recorded and your device movements.

❖ Portrait video: This helps you adject background of the shot to portrait videos.

❖ Director's view: Get you access to advanced features like switching between the lenses of your rear camera, locking on any subject in the view, and many more.

AR Zone

Get access to every of the Augmented Reality (AR) function at one place.

❖ From your 📷 Camera, you should slide to More, then you tap on AR Zone. These are the available features:

• AR Emojis Studios: Employ the AR tools for customization and creation of your My Emojis avatars.

• AR Emojis Camera: Employ your camera for the creation of your My Emojis avatars.

• AR Emojis Stickers: This adds up AR stickers into My Emojis avatars.

• AR Doodle: Helps you add handwritten notes or line drawings to the environment to enhance your videos and make it look better.

AR Doodle allows you to move with them by tracking faces & space.

- Deco Pic: Allows you decorate videos and pictures on real time using your camera.

- Quick measure: Allows you measure any items in centimeters or in inches with your camera.

The Space Zoom

Helps you capture clear, accurate pictures with as much as 100 times the magnification (only the Galaxy S 24 Ultra).

1. From your Camera, you should tap on any Zoom shortcuts for choosing any magnification settings.

- Whenever you capturing pictures in higher magnifications, you should center the target on your frame, then you tap on Zoom locks, to get accurate and fast zoom focusing.

2. Tap on Capture.

Record videos

You can record smooth lovable videos with your device camera.

1.   From your 🎥 Cameras, you should slide left or right to switch your shooting modes to a Video.

2.   Tap on ⦿ Record to start a recording of any video.

- To let you capture photos while you are recording, tap on ⊡ Capture.

- To temporarily halt your recording, tap on ‖ Pause. Then to resume your recording tap on ▪ Resume.

3.   Tap on ⦿ Stop, to stop your recording once you done recording.

Using the 360 audio recordings

With the 360 audios recordings, you can record immersive 3Ds sounds using Bluetooth headphones (separately sold).

1.   From your 🎥 Camera, you should tap on ⚙ Settings.

2.   Tap on Advanced videos options > then select the 360 audios recordings to activate.

Camera settings

To set up the settings of your camera's, utilize the icons in your camera's main screen & on your settings menu. Options may differ by your service provider.

❖ From your ⬤ Camera, tap on ⚙ Settings for the below selections:

Intelligent feature

- Scene optimizers: This adjusts automatically your colors configuration of your photos to match your subject matter

- Shots suggestions: Provide for you an on-screen direction to assist you in lining up wonderful shots.

- Scans QR codes: Detects QR codes automatically while your camera is being use.

Pictures

- Swipes on Shutter buttons to: This select whether or not to capture burst shots or to create a GIF once you swipe on your shutter to closest edge.

- Watermark: It Places a watermark in your photos' lower left corner.

- Advanced pictures option: Select various saving options & file formats.

- HEIF pictures: Helps you saves your photos as high proficiency images to your save space. This format might not be supported by certain sharing sites.

- Pro-mode pics format: Helps you choose a format you can save your Pro-mode pics in.

Selfie

- Save the selfies as preview: Lets you saves selfies the way they display on your preview without them flipping.

Video

- Auto FPS: Helps you record videos with more brightness in dim lighting condition, via automatically optimizing your frame rate when using Video mode.

- Video stabilization: Enable anti-shake, to maintain an uninterrupted focus when your camera moves.

- Advance videos options: Helps you improve your videos better by using advanced formats for recording.

- Highs efficiency videos: Helps record your videos in format of HEVC to your save. some sharing sites or devices might not support the format for playback.

❖ High bitrates videos (for Pro video): Use the Pro video shooting option to record videos at higher bits rates.

❖ HDR10+ videos: Use HDR10+ recording to optimize your videos. HDR10+ video must be supported by playback devices.

❖ Zoom-in microphone: When shooting videos, align the microphone's zoom with your camera's.

- ❖ 360 audios recordings: Allows you to record immersive 3D sound with Bluetooth headphones.

General

- Tracking with auto-focus: Maintain focus on a moving subject.

- Grid lines: Show the grid lines in your viewfinder to assist in composing an image or video.

- Location tags: For your photos & videos, add up GPS locations tags.

- Methods for shooting:

- ❖ Press the Volumes keys to: You can utilize your volume keys to Zoom in, record video, snap photos, adjust your system's volume.

- ❖ Voice commands: You can capture yourself saying key words.

- ❖ Floating shutters button: Helps in adding an additional shutter button which you may move across your screen.

❖ Show palm: To get your photo captured in few seconds, hold out your hand as your palm faces your camera.

• Settings for keep: Select whether to open Camera using the same filters, selfie angle, and shooting mode as previously used.

• Shutters sound: When snapping a photo, play a sound.

• Vibrations feedbacks: In your camera application, turn on vibrations as you press your screen.

• Privacy Notice: Access Samsung's privacy details.

• Permissions: Check your camera application's needed & optional permissions.

• Others [FSI] 🐢 Reset settings: This lets you reset your camera configuration. Contact us: Use Samsung Members to get in touch with Samsung support.

• About Camera: See information about applications & software.

Gallery

Navigate to your Gallery, to view all of your stored visual media on your smartphone. Pictures and videos can be viewed, edited, and managed. From your Apps, you should tap on  Gallery

Pictures

Today

Sort images into custom albums

Customize collections of pictures and videos

View pictures and videos

Viewing pictures

You may view your device's stored pictures using your Gallery application.

1.   From your ✱ Gallery, tap the Pictures.

2.   Tapping on pictures to view them. Then Swipe to your right or left to see any other photo or video.

- In order to utilize your Bixby Vision in your current photo, you should tap on ⦿ Bixby Vision.

- To mark any picture as one of your favorite, tap ♡ on Adds to Favorites.

❖ Select ⋮ more options to get the features that follows:

❖ Details: Lets you view and modify your image's information.

❖ Remastering picture: Employ the automatic images enhancements to refine your picture.

❖ Add up portrait effects: Use the slider to boost or reduce your background's visibility in your portrait shots.

❖ Copy into clipboard: Lets you copy and paste your image into a different application.

❖ Set as wallpaper: Make your picture to be your wallpaper.

❖ Moves to Secured Folder: Helps you move your picture into Secure Folders.

❖ Print: Send your picture onto any printer that is connected.

Editing your pictures

Use the editing tools in your Gallery to improve the look of your pictures.

1. From your ✸ Gallery, you should tap on Pictures.

2. Tap any picture to see them, then you should tap on ✏ Edit for the subsequent choices:

• ✴ Auto adjusts: Lets you employ automatic adjustment for enhanced pictures.

• ⬜ Transform: Adjust the image's general appearance by rotating, flipping, cropping, or applying other effects.

• ◐ Filters: Lets you add up color effects.

- ☼ Tone: Change your contrast, exposure, brightness, and other settings.

- ☺ Decorations: Let you add up stickers, text, or any hand drawn material.

- ⁝ More options: Provides more editing features.

3.   Revert: Revert the modifications made in order to get your original picture back.

4.   You should tap on Save once done.

Playing video

Watch the videos that are saved on your gadget. Videos can be viewed in detail and saved as favorites.

1.   From your ✿ Gallery, tap the Pictures.

2.   To watch a video, tap on it. To see more pictures or videos, swipe to the right or left.

3.   Tap on ♡ Adds to Favorites to add a video to your favorites list. Your album's Favorites tab now includes the video.

❖ Tap on ⋮ more options to get the features that follow:

❖ Details: Helps you view & edit details about your video.

❖ Launch in Video player: You can access and view this video in the default video player.

❖ Set up as wallpapers: Help you set up a video as your lock screen wallpaper.

❖ Move into Secured Folder: Let you add up videos into Secure Folder.

1.   Tap on ▶ Play video for playing your video.

Setting up your video brightness

You can enhance your videos image quality to relish brighter & much vivid color.

❖ From your Settings, you should tap on ◯ Advanced features > then tap on Video brightness, then select any option.

Editing video

You can edit your videos which are saved in your devices.

1. From your ✱ Gallery, tap on any video.

2. Tap on any video to check it out.

3. Tap on ✎ Edit, in order to utilize these tools:

- 🔊 Audio: Modify your video's volume & add music to the background.

- ▶ Play: See a preview of your edited video.

- ✂ Trim: Trim some video segments.

- ⬚ Transform: Adjust your video's overall appearance by rotating, flipping, cropping, or applying other modifications.

- ◐ Filters: With visual effects, you can simply enhance your video.

- ○ Tone: Modify exposure, contrast, brightness, and other settings.

- ☺ Decorations: Include hand-drawn materials, stickers, or other graphics.

- ⋮ More options: Get access to more editing tools.

- Revert: Remove the modifications made in order to get your original video back

- Tap on Save, then you tap confirm once prompted.

Sharing videos & pictures

Photos & videos can be shared via your Gallery application.

1.   From your Gallery, tap on a Pictures.

2.   Tap on ⋮ More options > then Edit and choose your photo or videos that you wish to share.

3.   Tap on ⋖ Share, then select an application or connection for sharing what you selected. Follow the directions.

Deleting pictures & videos

You may delete the pictures & the videos, which are stored in your device.

1.   From your ✳ Gallery, you should tap on ⋮ More options > Edit.

2.   Tap on images and videos to pick them.

110

3.   Tap on Delete, then you confirm once prompted.

Grouping similar images

By similarity You can organize your pictures & videos in your Gallery.

1.   From your ✱ Gallery, you should tap on Group with similar images.

2.   Tap on Ungroup similar image, in order to revert back to your default's Gallery views.

Taking screenshot

Take a photo of the screen. The Gallery app on your gadget automatically will create new Screenshots album.

❖ From any of your screen, press on & release your Side with Volume down buttons.

Using Palm swipe for capturing screenshots

You can utilize the palm swipe to capture images of your screen, as you swipe using hand edge across your screen, from one side to another side, maintaining contact with your screen.

1.   From your Settings, you should tap on
Advanced features > then select Motions & gestures >
then Palm swipes to capture.

2.   Tap on   to activate the feature.

Screenshots settings

You can always alter your screenshot settings.

❖ From your Settings, tap on   Advanced
   features > then Screenshots.

• Shows toolbars after capturing: Displays more
   options, once you are doing capturing a
   screenshot.

• Deleting after sharing from the toolbar:
   Screenshots are deleted automatically once
   they have been shared via your screenshot
   toolbar.

• Hide status & navigations bars: Helps hides
   your navigation or status bars on a screenshot.

- Format: Choose whether or not you would prefer any of your screenshots should be saved in JPG or as PNG files

- Saves screenshots in: Select a location for storing your screenshots.

Your Screen recorder

Record events in your device, take notes, and make a self-portrait video with your camera to send to loved ones.

1.   From your Quick Settings, you should tap on

⬚ Screen recorder.

2.   Select any sound setting, then you tap on Start recording.

3.   Then it counts down for three seconds before beginning to record. You can start recording right away by tapping Skip countdown.

- Tap on ✐ Draw then draw on your screen.

- Tap on ◤ Pointers to display any icon on your screen while utilizing your S Pen (Only on Galaxy S 24 Ultra).

- Tap on 👤 Selfies video to add recordings from the front camera.

4.   Tap on ⏹ Stop to end your recording. They are automatically uploaded to your Gallery's Screens Recordings albums.

Settings of the Screen recorder

You can manage your screen recorder's quality & sound settings.

- ❖ From your Settings, you should tap on ⚙ Advanced features > then select Screenshots & screen recorders.

- Sound: Let you select the sound to record when using your screen recorder.

- Video quality: Selecting a resolution. When choosing higher resolutions for better quality needs more storage space.

- Size of selfies video: To adjust your video overlay's size, drag your slider.

- Show touches and taps: Permit for the indication of screen touches and taps in recording.

- Saves screens recordings in: Select the location where you want to store the screen recordings.

Apps & Usage

Apps list shows every preloaded & the downloaded applications. Your application could be downloaded on your Galaxy and your Google Plays stores.

❖ From any Home screen, you should swipe your screen upward to reveal your Apps list.

Uninstalling or disabling applications

You can decide to uninstalled any applications on your device. Certain applications which are preloaded (those available default apps in your device) may only be deactivated. Disabled applications will be turned off, then hidden from your Apps list.

❖ From your Apps, you can touch & hold down an application, and then tap on the Uninstall/Disable.

Searching for apps

Whenever you are uncertain about where you will find an application or a particular setting, you may utilize your Search feature.

1.   From your Apps, you should tap on Search, and then type words or a word. When you type a matching applications or settings, there appears a results on your screen.

2.   Tap on the result to open that application.

TIP: You can always customize your search settings via tapping on the ⋮ More options > then Settings.

Sorting apps

You may customize the order of arrangement for list, or your App shortcuts could be listed in alphabetical order.

❖ From your Apps, tap on ⋮ More options > then Sort for the subsequent sorting options:

• Custom order: This let you arrange applications manually.

• Alphabetical order: Sort your applications alphabetically.

TIP: When applications are manually arranged (Custom order), your empty icons spaces may be removed via tapping on ⋮ More options > then Cleans up pages.

Creating & using folders

You may create folders for organizing your App shortcuts in your Apps list.

1.   From your Apps, you should touch & hold down any application shortcut, then you drag it over of another application shortcut till it gets highlighted.

2.   For creating the folder, release your application's shortcut.

- Folders name: Tittle your folder.

- Palette: Modify the color of the folder

- ✛ Add apps: Add more apps within your folder. After selecting your applications by tapping them, and then you tap Done.

3.   To close the folder, tap on ⟨ Back.

Copying folders to Home screens

You may copy any folder to any of your Home screens.

❖ From your Apps, you should touch & hold down any folder, then you tap on Adds to Home.

Deleting a folder

Whenever you delete any folder, your application shortcuts revert back to your Apps list.

1. From your Apps, you should touch & hold down any folder for delete.

2. Tap on Delete folder, then you confirm once prompted.

App settings

You can manage your preloaded and downloaded applications.

❖ From your Settings, you should tap on Apps. Then you tap on an option for customization:

• Choose default applications: You can select what applications you want to use for call making, sending messages, or going to internet sites, and many more.

- Samsung's application settings: Lets you see the list of Samsungs applications and allow you to also customize each setting.

- Your apps: You should tap any app to check out & update info on its privacy with its usage settings. These options may differ by app.

 TIP: When you want to reset your app options which has been altered, you should tap on ⋮ More options > then select Reset apps preference.

Calendar

The Calendar application can be linked to all your numerous online accounts to merge every of your calendars at a place.

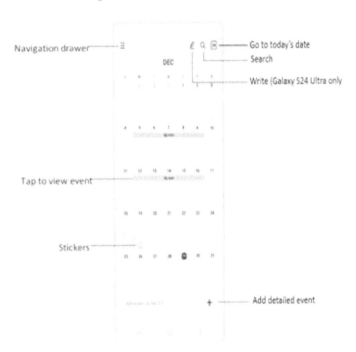

Adding up calendars

You can add your various accounts to your Calendar application.

1. From your Calendar, tap on the Navigation drawer.

2.   Tap on Manage calendars > the select ┬ Add account then choose any account type.

3.   Enter in information of your account and then follow the directions.

- **TIP:** Your accounts may additionally support your email, contacts, with even other features.

Styles of calendar alert

The Calendar application allows users to customize the style of their alerts.

1.   From your 🅛 Calendar, you should tap on ≡ Navigation drawer > then on Calendar ⚙ settings > then select Alert style.

These are the available options

- Light: Hear a brief sound and get a notification.

- Medium: Hear a brief sound and receive an entire screen alert.

- Strong: When you dismiss it, a full-screen notification & ring sound will continue to sound until dismissed.

2. Based on your alert style that was previously selected. The subsequent sound options are available:

- Short sound: Select your alert sound, for your Light / Medium alert types.

- Long sound: Select your alerts sound to use for your Strong alerts style.

Creating events

Employ your Calendar for creation of events.

1. From your Calendar, tap on Add detailed events for adding an event.

2. Enter your details for that event, then tap on Save.

Deleting events

You can delete events in your Calendar.

1.   From your 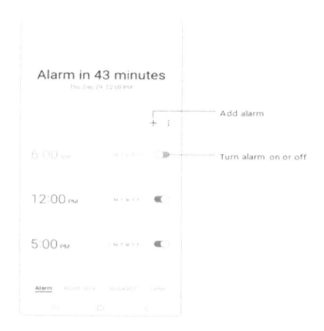 Calendar, you should tap any event, and then tap on it again for editing it.

2.   Tap on Delete, then you confirm once prompted.

Clock

Your Clock app includes alarm-setting and time-tracking features.

Alarm

You can Set up a recurring alarm or one-time and select how you would be notified through the options provided, when using your Alarm tab.

1.   From your ⦿ Clock, you should tap on ✝ Add alarm.

2.   To set up your alarm, you should tap on these below items:

- Time: Set up your alarm time.

- Day: Select days for your alarm.

- Alarm name: Type in a name for your alarm.

- Alarm sound: Select what sound you want ring as your alarm then you drag on your slider to setup volume of your alarm.

- Vibration: Select whether or not your alarm should include the vibration alert.

- Snooze: Allows to snoozing. Let you choose intervals & repeats values for your alarms during snoozing.

3.   Tap on Save for saving your alarm.

TIP: To start your sleep routine, set up bedtime reminders, then have your device go into sleep mode automatically, you should tap on ⋮ More options > then Sets Sleep modes schedules.

Deleting alarms

You may delete your created alarms, do these:

1.   From your ⊙ Clock, you should touch & hold down any alarm.

2.   Tap on 🗑 Delete.

Alert settings

Whether or not your sound mode has been configured to Vibrate or Mute, you can configure your smartphone to vibrate when alarms and timers goes off.

1.   From your ⊙ Clock, you should tap on ⋮ More options > then Settings.

2.   Tap on Silence alarms while system sounds are turned off to activate this feature.

Alarms settings

It is possible to get notifications about upcoming alarms.

1.   From your ⊙ Clock, you should tap on ⋮ More options > then Settings.

2.   Tap on an Upcoming alarms notice to select what number of the minutes prior to upcoming alarms.

Chapter 3
Contacts

Manage and store your contact list. With personal accounts you've integrated into your device, it may synchronize. Calendars, email, and various other features might also be supported by accounts.

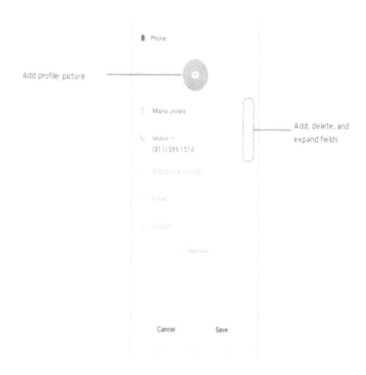

Creating contact

1.   From your 🔘 Contacts, tap on ✛ Create contact.

2.   Type in details for your contact, then you tap Save.

Editing contact

When you are editing any contact, you may add new fields to your contact's list of details or tap on a field to change or remove information.

1.   From your 🔘 Contacts list, tap on a contact.

2.   Tap on ✎ Edit.

3.   Tap on any of your fields to change/ delete, add information.

4.   Tap on Save.

Favorites

Whenever you select your contacts as your favorites, they will be grouped on top of the contact list, making them to be very accessible from your other applications.

1.   From your 🔘 Contacts, tap on a contact.

2.   Tap on ☆ the Favorites to select that contact as one of your favorites.

- To remove any of your contact from the Favorites, tap on ☆ Favorites.

Sharing contact

Using a variety of sharing tools and services, you can share any contact to other people.

1.   From your ⊖ Contacts, you should tap on a contact.

2.   Tap on ⋘ Share.

3.   Tap on either Text or vCard files (VCF).

4.   Select a method of sharing and then follow the directions.

TIP: To instantly share contact details with friends and family, select More > then QR code while viewing the contact. When you make changes to your contact information boxes, your QR code is automatically updated.

Show contacts while you share content

From inside any application, you can share your contents instantly with contacts. Your frequently used contacts are shown on your Share window once they are enabled.

❖ From your Settings, tap on Advanced features > then Show contacts while sharing contents, then tap on to activate this feature.

Using Groups

You may utilize the groups for organizing your contacts.

Creating groups

You can create your personal contact groups.

1. From your Contacts, you should tap on Show navigations menu > then Groups.

2. Tap on Create group, then you tap on fields to type information about that group:

- Group name: You type in any name for your new group.

- Group ringtone: You may customize your group sound.

- Add member: After choosing which contacts to include in the newly created group, tap Done.

3. Tap on Save.

Adding or removing group contacts

Contacts can be added or removed from a group as much as you want.

- ❖ From your 🔘 Contacts, tap on ☰ Shows navigations menu > then select Groups, then you tap on a group.

- To 🗑 remove any contact, press and hold any contact to pick it, then press Remove to remove it.

- If you want to add up any contact of your tap on Edit > then select Add member, then you tap on that contacts that you wish to add. Once finished, tap on Done > then Save.

Sending messages to groups

You can send text messages group members.

1.   From your ⚇ Contacts, you should tap on ☰ Show navigations menu > then Groups, then you tap on a group.

2.   Tap on the More options > the Send message.

Sending emails to group

You send emails to your group members.

1.   From your ⚇ Contacts, tap on ☰ Shows navigations menu > then on Groups, then you tap on a group.

2.   Tap on the More options > then Send email.

3.   Tap on contacts to choose them, or you tap on All checkbox which is on top of your screen to choose all, then you tap Done.

❖ Members of the group are displayed only if they have a personal email address on their record.

4.   Pick any email account of yours then follow the directions.

Deleting group

For deleting any group that created do these actions.

1.　　From your ⊖ Contacts, tap on ☰ Shows navigations menu > then select Groups, then you tap on a group.

2.　　Tap on the ⋮ More options > then Delete group.

- To delete group only, tap on Delete groups only.
- To delete your group along with your group contacts, tap on Delete groups & the move members to trash.

Managing your contacts

It is possible to link several contacts into a single contact entry and export or import contacts.

Merge contacts

Combine contact details from several sources into a single contact. When you link entries into one contact.

1.　　From your ⊖ Contacts, tap on ☰ Shows navigations menu > then select Manage contacts.

2.   Tap on Merge contacts. Afterwards, contacts that have identical names, phone numbers, and email addresses will be presented together.

3.   Tap on your contacts for selecting them, then you tap on Merge.

Importing contacts

You can Import contacts into device as a vCards files (VCF).

1.   From your ⊖ Contacts, you should tap on ≡ Shows navigations menu > then Manage contacts.

2.   Tap on Import contacts, then you follow the directions.

Exporting contacts

You can export contacts in your devices as a vCard files (VCF).

1.   From your ⊖ Contacts tap on ≡ Show navigation menu > then select Manage contacts.

2.   Tap on Export contacts, then you follow the directions.

Synchronize contacts

You can maintain updated contacts across all your accounts.

1. From your 👤 Contacts tap on ☰ Shows navigations menu > then select Manage contacts.

1. Tap on Sync contacts.

Deleting contacts

You can delete single contact and several contacts.

1. From your 👤 Contacts, you should touch & hold down any contact of yours to select.

- You may also tap on other contacts for selection for deletion.

2. Tap on 🗑 Delete, then you confirm once prompted.

Deleting contacts

You may delete just one contact or several contacts at once.

1. From your 👤 Contacts, you should touch & hold down any contact then select.

- You may also tap on any other contacts you delete, to select.

2. Tap on 🗑 Delete, then you confirm once prompted to.

The emergency contacts

Even with a locked device, you can still dial your emergency contacts.

- ❖ From your Settings, you should tap on Safety & emergency > then Emergency contacts.

- Add member: You can select contacts in your device as the emergency contacts.

- Shows on the Locks screens: Displays your emergency contacts in your Lock screens for fast access during an emergency.

Chapter 4
The Internet

For your mobile device, Samsung's Internet is an easy-to-use, dependable, and fast online browser. Discover enhanced browsing speed, privacy protection, and enhanced browsing features with safer Web browsing options.

Browser tabs

You can use tabs for viewing several web pages simultaneously

* ❖ From your ⬤ Internet, tap on 🔲 Tabs > then New tab.

* • To close any tab, you should tap on 🔲 Tabs > ⊗ to Close tab.

Creating Bookmark

To easily retrieve your favorite webpages, you should bookmark them.

* ❖ From your ⬤ Internet, you should tap on ☆ the Add to the bookmarks to keep your open webpage.

Opening Bookmark

You can quickly open any web site from your Bookmarks page.

1.   From your ⬤ Internet, you should tap on ☆ Bookmarks.

2.   Tap on bookmark entry.

Saving web page

On your Samsung Internet application, there are multiple options for you to save any webpage.

❖ From your ⊖ Internet, tap on ☰ Tools > then Add page, for the subsequent options:

• Bookmarks: Add a web page in your list of bookmarks.

• Quick access: See a listing of frequently visited or bookmarked webpages.

• Home screen: On your Home screen, make shortcut to your webpage.

• Saved pages: To access webpage content offline, that are saved in your device.

View history

You can see all the list of your newly visited site:

❖ From your ⊖ Internet, you should tap on ☰ Tools > then History.

TIP: To wipe clean browsing history, you should tap on ⋮ More options > then Clear history.

Sharing pages

You can always share web pages with those on your contact list.

❖ From your ⬤ Internet, tap on ≡ Tools > then select Share, then you follow the direction prompts.

Secret mode

Viewed pages in secret mode don't appear in your search or browser history and don't leave any cookies or other traces on your mobile device. Compared to regular tab windows, secret tabs are deeper in color.

Once you close your secret tab, those downloaded files stay on the device.

1.   From your ⬤ Internet, tap on ⬛ Tabs > then Turn on your secret mode.

2.   Tap on Start to start browsing on secret mode.

Settings of Secret mode

Employ a biometric lock or password to access secret mode.

1.   From your ⬤ Internet, tap on ⬛ Tabs.

2.   Tap   on More options > then your Secret modes settings for these options:

- Use Password: To use biometrics and activate secret mode, establish a password.

- Reset Secret mode: This restores defaults and clear any data stored in secret mode.

Turning off your secret mode

You can always turn off secret mode & resume your regular browsing.

❖ From your Internet, you should tap on Tabs > the Turn off the secret mode.

Your Internet settings

You can change the settings related to your Internet application.

❖ From your Internet, tap on Tools > then Settings.

Messages

Use your Messages application to stay in touch with those you know by sending hellos, sharing images, and sending emojis. Service providers may offer several options.

❖ Under messages, click create new message.

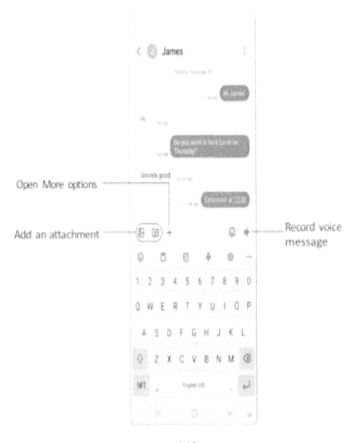

Search Message

You can easily to find a message, by using your search feature.

1.   From your Messages, you should tap on Search.

2.   Type keywords on your Search field, then you tap on Search on your keyboard.

Delete conversations

You may remove conversion history via deleting such conversations.

1.   From your Messages, you should tap on More options > the Delete.

2.   Tap on every conversation you wish to delete.

3.   Tap on Delete all, then you confirm once you are prompted.

Emergency messaging

You may Send messages to all emergency contact of yours, which can include audio & pictures.

1.   From your Settings, tap on Safety & emergency >then Emergency SOS. Turn on to begin these actions via pressing on your key 5 times:

- Countdown: Decide how many seconds you want to wait prior activating emergency procedures.

- Make an emergency call: Select which number to use when making emergency call.

- share information with emergency contacts: Turn on to give your emergency contacts your location.

TIP: Additionally, you may activate your Emergency SOS by pushing down your Side & Volume button, then tapping on Emergency call.

Emergency sharing

You can send messages with audio and pictures to emergency contacts.

1. From your Settings, you should tap on 🔘 Safety & emergency > then select Emergency sharing. Select what you want to share with emergency contacts when help is needed:

- Attach pictures: You can capture and send photos using your rear & front cameras.

- Attaching audio recordings: Lets you record & send a 5 seconds audio.

2. Tap on Starts emergency sharing in order to send your chosen media to emergency contacts.

Messaging settings

You can configure your settings for your multimedia messages and text.

- ❖ From your 🔘 Messages, tap on More options > then on Settings.

Emergency alerts

Your emergency alerts warn you of forthcoming threats with other circumstances. Your emergency alerts messages are free of charge.

❖ From your Settings, tap on Safety & emergency > then Wireless Emergencies Alerts in order to customize your notifications for your emergency alerts.

TIP: You may also access your Emergency alerts in the Notifications. From your Settings, tap on Notifications > then select Advanced settings > then Wireless Emergency Alert.

My Files

You can manage and view files which are kept in your device, these files may include music, videos, documents, sound clips and many more. You may also retrieve and manage the files stored in your device cloud accounts, also your SD card, when supported.

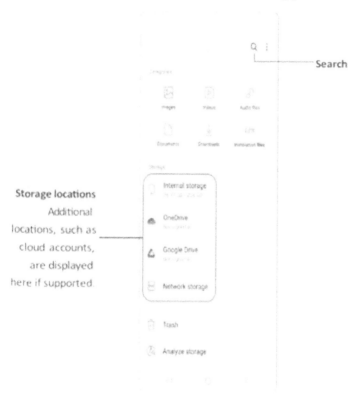

The File groups

The files stored on your device are ordered into these below groups:

- Recent files: View recently accessed files.

❖ This option only shows up when you have accessed one or many files recently.

- Categories: Let you view the files on basis of their file type.

- Storage: Let you view files stored in your device, cloud accounts, and optional Memory card.

❖ Your Cloud accounts may differ based on services you are sign to.

- Analyze storage: Checks what is occupying your space from your device storage

Settings up My Files

You can utilize My Files settings for customizing your files management selections and many more. These options may differ by your service provider.

❖ From your ⬜ My Files, tap on ⋮ More options > the select Settings for these options:

- Cloud accounts: Helps connect to, with managing cloud services.

- File management: You can always customize how your files should be presented, deleted, or even access your mobile data.

❖ Analyze storage: Allows you select any file size for flagging whenever you analyzing your storage.

- Privacy: Allows you view permissions of My Files.

Chapter 5
Phone

Your Phone application lets you do more than just making phone calls, you can explore your advanced features for calling. For more details, you can get to your services provider. The actual look for the screen of your Phone application and the available options differs depending on service provide

Calls

Your Phone application lets you receive and to place calls from Home screen of your device, Contacts, Recents tab, and more.

Making calls

You can utilize your phone for making and receiving calls from any of your Home screen.

- ❖ From your 📞 Phone, enter any number on your keypad, then you tap on 📞 Call.
- • Tap on Keypad when your keypad does not show up.

Making calls from your Recents

Every of your incoming, missed and outgoing calls are documented on your Call log.

1.   From your 📞 Phone, you should tap on Recents, so as to display the list your recent calls.

2.   Tap on a contact, then you tap on 📞 Call.

Making calls from your Contacts

You can call any contact in your Contacts application.

❖ From your ⬤ Contacts, you can swipe your finger on any contact towards the right in order to call that contact.

Answering a call

Once you receive a call, your phone will ring out, then your caller's name or number will displayed. If at the time you receive a you were using some other application, you will see a pop-up screen displayed for your incoming call.

❖ On your incoming calls screen, you should drag on ☏ Answer towards your right to receive your call.

TIP: On your pop-up screen of incoming calls, tap on ☏ Answer for answering your call.

Declining calls

You may decide to decline any incoming calls of yours, while you might be utilizing another application. You will see a pop-up screen displayed for your incoming call.

❖ On your incoming calls screen, you should drag on ⌢ Decline towards your left-side of screen for rejecting that call, then you send into your voicemail.

TIP: On your incoming pop-up screen, you can tap on Decline for rejecting your call, then send it into your voicemail.

Declining with message

You may decide to decline any incoming call, using a response of text message.

❖ On your incoming calls screen, you should drag on Send message towards the up and then choose a message.

TIP: On your pop-up screen of your incoming call, tap on Send message then you choose a message.

Ending call

❖ Tap on ⌣ End call once you are set to end a call.

Actions during a call

Adjusting your call volume, switching your call to a speaker or headset, and even do various task during on call.

- ❖ Press on your Volume buttons for increasing/decreasing your volume.

Switching between speaker/headset

You can either listen to your call with your speaker or using any Bluetooth® headset (this not included).

- ❖ Tap on ◁)) Speaker to listen to your caller with your speaker or you tap on ⅄ Bluetooth and hear your caller on any Bluetooth headset.

Multitask

Your lively call will be indicated on your status bar, when you leave your call screen to another application.

To return back to your call screen

- ❖ Drag on your Status bar downward to display your Notification panel then you tap on your call.

To end call when multitasking

❖ Drag on your Status bar downward for displaying your Notification panel, then you tap on ⊙ End call.

Call background

Choose a video or picture that display when you are making or receiving a call.

❖ From your ⓒ Phone, you should tap on ⦙ More options > then select Settings ⦂ and then Call background for these options:

• Layout: Specify how caller information is shown when the individual possesses a profile photo.

• Background: Select a picture to show when you are on the phone.

Settings call pop-up

Calls may appear as pop-up windows when you're using other applications.

❖ From your ⓒ Phone, you should tap on ⦙ More options > then Settings > then select Call display when you are using applications. These are the available options below:

- full screens: Helps display your Phone app's entire screen will show a call that's incoming.

- Small pop-up: Show a pop-up on your screen top when a call is incoming.

- Mini pop-up: Show a mini pop-up when there is a call coming in.

- Keep calls on pop-up: If you want to retain calls on your pop-up even after they've been answered, turn on this feature.

Manage your calls

Your call log keeps records of your calls. You may use voicemail, block numbers, and set up your speed dials.

Call log

Your Call log stores the phone calls numbers you might have dialed, missed, and received.

- ❖ From your Phone, you should tap on Recents. There's a list with recent calls shown.

Your caller's name appears if they are in your list of Contacts.

Save contact from the recent call

If you want to update or create a contact, use details from a recent call on the Contacts list.

1.   From your ● Phone, tap on Recents.

2.   Tap on Add to your contacts after tapping the call that has the information you wish to store in the Contacts list.

3.   Select the option to create a new contacts / Update an existing contact.

Deleting recorded calls

You can always delete your Call logs entries:

1.   From your ● Phone, you should tap on Recents.

2.   Touch & hold on calls you desire to delete in your Call log.

3.   Tap on 🗑 Delete.

Blocking number

When you add any caller on your blocked list, you prevent future calls via that number from reaching you on voicemail and you do not receive any messages.

1.   From your 🅒 Phone, then tap on Recents.

2.   Tap on ⃠ the caller which you wish to put to your Block list, then tap on 🅘 Details.

3.   Tap on ⦂ Block, or you tap More > then Block contact, after which you confirm once prompted.

TIP: You may also alter settings of your Block list. From your 🅒 Phone, you should tap ⦂ More options > then Settings > and then select Block numbers.

Speed dial

A contact can have shortcut number assigned to them so they can speed dial their number.

1.   From your 🅒 Phone, tap on Keypad > then you tap ⦂ more options > then select Speed dial number. Your screen of Speed dials numbers displays your kept speeds dial number.

2.　　Tap on any unassigned number.

- Tap on ▼ Menu to pick an alternative Speeds dial numbers from the one next on the sequence.

- Voicemail is designated for number 1.

3.　　To assign any contact to a number, enter in any name/ number or you tap on 👤 to Add from your Contacts.

Your Speed dial numbers bar shows your chosen contact.

Making calls using your Speed dial
You can use Speed dial to place a call.

- ❖ From your 🅒 Phone, you should touch & hold your Speeds dial numbers.

- Enter your first initial digits of your Speed dialed number and hold your last digit if it has an additional digit.

Removing Speed dialed numbers
An allocated Speed dialed number can be removed.

1. Select More options > then on Speed dials numbers from the Phone menu.

2. Select that contact you wish to remove of your Speed dial by tapping Delete.

Emergency calls

Regardless of condition of your phone's service, you may call the emergency number within your region. The only calls you can make when your phone has not been turned on are emergency ones.

1.   From your Phone, you should enter your emergency phone number (in the North America is 911) and then tap on Call.

2.   Complete the call. The majority of in-call features are available to you during this kind of call.

TIP: Even with your phone locked, anybody may utilize your phone to make a call urgent help during an emergency by dialing your emergency number. Your emergency call features are the only one that can be accessed by the caller when their screen is locked. The phone is still secured in its entirety.

Phone settings

You can change your phone application's settings using these settings.

❖ From your ☺ Phone, you should tap on ⋮ More options > then Settings.

Optional call services

These calling services could be supported by your wireless provider & service package.

Placing multi-party calls

While on the phone, place another call. Service providers may offer several options.

1. From your active call, you should tap on ✛ Add call any called to dial your second call.

2. Dial your new number then you tap ☺ Call. Once your call has been answered:

- Tap on ⬚ Swap or On hold down number for switching between 2 calls.

- Tap on ⤳ Merge to listen to both your callers the same time. (multi-conferencing)

161

Making video calls

For video calls do these:

On Phone, type in any number, then you tap on Meet or you Video call, maybe even Video call.

Note: Video calls are not supported by every device. The recipient can choose to answer the call as a conventional voice call or accept it has video call

Effects of your video calls

Using the available apps, you can modify or blur your background while on a video conversation.

1.   From your Settings, you should tap on Advanced features > then select Video call effects.

2.   Tap on to activate this feature.

3.   Select any available options:

- Background colors: You can alter your virtual backgrounds into a solid color automatically depending on what's surrounding you.

- Backgrounds images: Let you pick a picture within your photos for using as video calls background.

Wi-Fi calling

You can make calls using a Wi-Fi when connected to any Wi-Fi network.

1.   From your Phone, you should tap on More options > then Settings > then select Wi-Fi calling.

2.   Tap on to activate this feature.

3.   Follow the directions configure and set up your Wi-Fi calling.

Samsung Notes

You can create notes having text, audio recordings, pictures with footnotes, and music using Samsung Notes. Utilizing social networking sites, sharing your notes is made easy.

Creating notes

You can add up text, voice recordings, pictures, and many more.

1.   From your Samsung Notes, you should tap on Add.

2.   Use your text options for creating contents.

Voice recordings

You can create voice recordings with annotations that are ideal for meetings or classes. While you record audios, take notes. The matching text is scrolled to in sync with the playback.

1.   From your Samsung Notes, you should tap on Add.

2.   Tap on   Insert > then select Voice recording.

3.   Utilize your text options for creating contents while an audio is currently being recorded.

Editing notes

You can edit your created notes.

1. From your ⬜ Samsung Notes, you should tap on any note to view.

2. Tap on ✐ Edit then make your changes.

3. Whenever you are done, you should tap on ‹ Navigate up.

Notes options

You may sort, edit, or even manage notes.

❖ From your ⬜ Samsung Notes, these are the available option:

• ⬜Import PDF: Let you open any PDF in your Samsung Notes.

• ⃝ Search: Helps you search for keyword.

• ⋮ More options:

❖ Edit: Help you choose notes to delete, share, save as a file, lock, or even move.

❖ View: Enable you to switch between list, Grid, or Simple list.

❖ Pins favorites to the top: Let you place marked notes which are your favorite at top of your main page.

Notes menu

Your notes can be viewed categorically.

❖ From your 🔲 Samsung Notes, you should tap on ☰ Shows navigation menu using these below options:

• ⚙ Settings: You can check out the settings for your Samsung Notes application.

• All notes: Lets you view all your notes.

• Shared notebooks: Allows you to see the notebooks shared among your contacts list via your Samsung's accounts.

• Trash: Let you view your deleted notes, at least up to fifteen days.

• Folders: Helps you view notes as groups.

• Manage folders: Let you add up, remove, or organize your folders.

Chapter 6

Settings

Accessing your Settings

Your device's settings can be accessed in a few different ways.

- From any of your Home screen, you should swipe downward then tap on ⚙ Settings.

- From Applications, you should tap on ⚙ Settings.

Searching for Settings

You may look for a setting when you are unsure of its precise location.

1.   From your Settings, tap on 🔍 Search, then enter in your keywords.

2.   Tap on an entry to navigate to the setting.

Connections

Manage the connections that your device has with different other devices and networks.

Wi-Fi

If you want to browse the Internet with no use of your mobile data, you may connect device via a Wi-Fi network.

1. From your Settings, you should tap on Connections > then select Wi-Fi, then you tap on to enable your Wi-Fi and to scan for networks available.

2. Tap on a network, then you type in a password when required.

3. Tap on Connect.

Connecting to hidden Wi-Fi networks

In the event that a scan does not reveal the desired Wi-Fi network, you can still establish a connection by manually inputting its details. Before you start, ask your network's Wi-Fi admin for the password and name.

1.   From your Settings, tap on ⦿ Connections > then Wi-Fi, then you tap on ⬎ to enable Wi-Fi.

2.   Tap on ┼ Add network on bottom of your list.

3.   Enter the details about your Wi-Fi network:

- Network name: Enter in the precise name of your network.

- Security: Choose security option in your list, and then enter your password when required.

- Password: Type in your network password.

- Hidden networks: You can insert in hidden network.

- View more: Specify other advanced variables, including proxy and IP settings.

4. Tap on Save.

TIP: Using the camera on your device, scan a QR code and connect to WiFi connection by tapping on ▦ Scan QR code.

Wi-Fi Direct

The Wi-Fi Direct allows devices to share data using Wi-Fi.

1.   From your Settings, you tap on 📶 Connections > then Wi-Fi, then you tap on ⬛ to enable your Wi-Fi.

2.   Tap on ⋮ More options > the select Wi-Fi Direct.

3.   Tap on device, then you follow the direction to connect.

Disconnecting from the Wi-Fi Direct

You can disconnect from any WIFI Direct device, following these steps:

❖ From your Settings, then tap on 📶 Connections > then on Wi-Fi >then tap ⋮ More options > select Wi-Fi Direct. Tap on that device so you can disconnect from it.

Settings for Intelligent Wi-Fi

You can search up your smartphone's network address, manage your saved networks, and set up connections to different kinds of hotspots & WiFi networks. Service providers may offer several options.

1.   From your Settings, tap on Connections > Wi-Fi, then you tap on to enable your Wi-Fi.

2.   Tap on More options > then Intelligent Wi-Fi use these options:

- Switch to mobile data: If this feature is turned on, your smartphone will always use mobile data when your Wi-Fi connection is unreliable. It reverts to Wi-Fi when your signal strength is high.

- Switching to better Wi-Fi networks: Helps you switch automatically to more dependable, faster or even more stable WIFI networks.

- Turns Wi-Fi off/on automatically: In places you use frequently, it turns on your Wi-Fi.

- Shows network quality information: Show network details on list of accessible Wi-Fi networks, such as stability and speed.

- Prioritize real-times data: Video calls, games, and other lag-sensitive tasks should be given network priority.

- Detects suspicious networks: Receive notifications when activity on the active Wi-Fi network is deemed suspicious.

- Wi-Fi power save mode: This activate a WIFI traffic analysis to decrease your battery usage.

- Auto-Hotspots connections: When a Wi-Fi hotspot is detected, it will automatically connect to it.

- Intelligent Wi-Fi: Check out the version of Intelligent Wi-Fi.

Your settings for advanced Wi-Fi

You may look up your smartphone's network address, manage your saved networks, and set up connections to different kinds of Wi-Fi connections & hotspots. Service providers may offer several options.

1.   From your Settings, you should tap on

Connections > then Wi-Fi, then you tap on ⬛ to

enable your Wi-Fi.

2.   Tap on ⁞More options > then select Advanced

settings use these options:

- synchronize with Samsung Cloud or account:
  synchronize your Wi-Fi profiles together with
  Samsung account.

- Show up Wi-Fi pop-ups: This helps in alerting
  you that there is an available Wi-Fi once
  opening applications.

- WiFi/network notifications: Get notifications
  whenever open networks in reach are detected.

- Manage networks: See the Wi-Fi networks
  you've saved and set up which ones to
  automatically reconnect with to or forget.

- Wi-Fi off or on history: See which applications
  have recently enabled or disabled your Wi-Fi.

- Hotspot 2.0: When using Wi-Fi networks which support the Hotspot 2.0, connect to them automatically.

- Installing networks certificates: Helps in installation of authentication certificates for the network.

Bluetooth

Your device can be paired with other Bluetooth-capable devices, such as car infotainment systems or Bluetooth headphones. The devices will remember one another and share data without requiring the passkey to be entered again after a pairing has been established.

1.   From your Settings, you should tap on Connections > then Bluetooth, then you tap on to enable Bluetooth.

2.   Tap on a device then you follow the direction to connect.

TIP: When you are sharing any file, you should tap on Bluetooth to utilize this feature.

Renaming paired devices

You may choose to rename any paired device, so that you can easily recognize them.

1. From your Settings, you should tap on Connections > then tap on Bluetooth, then you tap on to enable Bluetooth.

2. Tap on Settings which is next to your device name, then you tap on Rename.

3. Type in new name, after which tap Rename.

Unpairing from Bluetooth devices

Whenever you unpair your device Bluetooth from a device, those two devices will not recognize themselves any more, you will have to pair them again for you to be able connect to that device.

1. From your Settings, tap on Connections > then Bluetooth, then you tap on to enable your Bluetooth.

2. You should tap on Settings which is next to your device, then you tap on Unpair.

3. Tap on Unpair for confirmation.

Your Advanced Bluetooth options

Your Advanced menu offers more Bluetooth features.
Service providers may offer several options.

1.   From your Settings, tap on 🛜 Connections >
then Bluetooth.

2.   Tap on the Advanced settings or you tap on ⋮
More options > then select Advanced setting use these
options:

- Synchronize with Samsung Cloud or account:
  You can Synchronize files which are
  transferred via your Bluetooth to Samsung's
  account.

- Ringtones sync: When a Bluetooth-connected
  device receives a call, use the ringtone that is
  configured in your device.

- Bluetooth Controls history: See which
  applications have lately used Bluetooth.

- Blocking pairings requests: Put more devices
  in the block pair list.

- Bluetooth scans history: See which
  applications have recently searched for close-

by Bluetooth devices & helps Manage your Bluetooth features application.

Dual audio

Two Bluetooth audio's device that are connected can receive audio playback from your mobile device.

1.   Connect your device to Bluetooth-enabled audio devices.

2.   Select Media output from your Notification panel.

3.   Under your Audio output simply tap on the icon next to both of them, for playing audio through any of your two audio devices.

NFC & payments

You may communicate with a different device via NFC (Near Fields Communication) without establishing a network connection. Some payment applications, including Android Beam, employ a similar technology. The device you are transmitting to must be four centimeters away from your device and must support NFC.

❖ From your Settings, tap on Connections > then select NFC & contactless payments, then you tap on to enable this feature.

Tap & pay

You can employ NFC payment application for payments via pressing your device to a supported credit cards viewer.

1. From your Settings, tap on Connections > then NFC & contactless payments, then you tap on to enable NFC.

2. Tap on Contactless payments in order to view your default payment application.

• To employ the use a different payment application, you should tap on any available application to select it.

• To employ the use of a payment application which is open, you should tap on Pay with the currently open application.

179

- To setup a different payment service to be your default, you should tap on Others, then you tap on service which you prefer.

Ultra-wideband

You can identify the exact locations of close-by devices. Options may differ by your service provider.

❖ From your Settings, you should tap on Connections > then select Ultra-wideband (UWB) for activating this function.

Airplane mode

All network connections, including Bluetooth, Wi-Fi, mobile data, calling, and texting, are disabled when your device is in airplane mode. You may enable both your Bluetooth and Wi-Fi in your Settings or even from your Quick Settings pane whenever Airplane mode is on.

❖ From your Settings, tap on Connections > then on Airplane mode, then you tap on to turn on feature.

Note: Federal and municipal laws and regulations may apply to the usage of mobile phones on ships and aircraft. All network connectivity will be disabled when in airplane mode. Airplane mode can be used to disable ultra-wideband (UWB), which is not allowed on board ships or airplanes. Considering how and when you can use the device, always heed crew instructions and confirm with the relevant authorities.

SIM manager

You may be able to control dual mobile accounts without you being with two devices by using an eSIM (which is embedded SIM) or dual SIM (two of which are physical SIMs cards) that are supported by your service plan and wireless services providers. Options differ depending on the service provider.

Dual SIM-capable devices have 2 SIM cards slots. If supported, it might additionally comprise a micro-SD card's slot as additional storage. After launch, software updates for dual SIM-capable devices will activate your integrated dual SIM ability.

It is possible to configure devices which support the eSIM such that it operates without the actual SIM card within the device. It makes it possible for either an eSIM or your actual SIM card to be utilized for the voice call/text & data. After launch, software updates for eSIM-capable devices will allow the built-in eSIM functionality.

- ❖ From your Settings, you should tap on Connections > then SIM manager using these below options:

- SIM cards: Enable, View, disable, or renaming the physical SIMs card that are installed on your device.

- eSIMs: Tap on ╋ Add eSIM for signing up for fresh eSIM mobile plan or for adding plan from a previous device.

- Primary SIM: Assign a primary SIM card to be utilized for data, messages, and phone calls while utilizing multi

- More SIMs settings: You can tap to discover more SIM card management options.

Using Mobile networks

Utilize your mobile networks to set up your device for using mobile data and connect via mobile networks. Service providers may offer several options.

- ❖ From your Settings, tap on Connections > then Mobile networks.

- Mobile data: Turn on your usage of mobile data.

- Internationals data roamings: this changes the text, voices and data roaming setup for the international roaming.

- Data roamings access: You can set up access to your mobile networks whenever you roaming.

- Data roamings: It allows data usage when roaming on another mobile network.

- Enhanced Calling: This permits enhanced communication via utilizing LTE data.

- System select: let you modify your CDMA roamings modes, when appropriate for the service provider.

- Access Points Names: Select/add APNs, that have network settings that your device requires for connecting to your provider.

- Networks operators: Picks the available, with the preferred networks.

- Mobile networking diagnostics: Gather diagnostic along with the usage-data for troubleshooting.

- Network extenders: This let you search for cells which could extend your device network connection.

TIP: For help in managing connection settings which could have an impact on your monthly payment, utilize these services.

Data usage

Verify how much data you are currently using on your mobile device and Wi-Fi. Additionally, your limits and warnings can be customized.

- ❖ From your Settings, tap on Connections > then select Data usage.

Turning on your Data saver

You can reduce your data usage by using Data Saver, which stops applications from receiving and transmitting data on the background.

1. From your Settings, you should tap on Connections > then Data usage > then select Data saver.

2. Tap on to enable Data saver.

    •   To let certain applications to get unlimited data usage, you should tap on Allowed to use-data while Data-saver is turned on, then you tap on next to every app to define restrictions.

Monitoring your mobile data

You can set limitations and restrictions to customize access to the mobile data. Options could differ depending on the service provider.

    ❖   From your Settings, you should tap on Connections > then select Data usage. These are the available options:

- Mobile data: Utilize your plan's mobile data.

- International data roaming: When roaming abroad, activate the services of mobile data.

- Mobile data for only applications: Helps you configure applications to use mobile date always, even while your device might be connected to a wireless network.

- Mobile's data usage: Check usage of data over time using mobile connections. Both the overall usage and the usage by application could be view.

- Data warning and billing cycle: Adjust your monthly date to coincide with your billing date provided by your services provider.

Monitoring your Wi-Fi data

By customizing your usage limits & networks, you could restrict the access your Wi-Fi data.

1.   From your Settings, you should tap on Connections > then Data usage.

2.   Tap on Wi-Fi data's usages to see your data-usage over Wi-Fi connections for certain time period.

You may check your total usage and the usage by your app.

Using your Mobile hotspot

Your mobile hotspot utilizes your data subscription for creating Wi-Fi networks which may be utilize by several devices.

1.   From your Settings, tap on Connections > then Mobile hotspot & tethering > tap Mobile hotspot.

2.   Tap on to enable your Mobile hotspot.

3.   On that device you wish to connect to, turn on Wi-Fi and Choose your device's wireless hotspot. To connect, enter the password for the mobile hotspot.

- Connected devices will be listed under heading of Connected devices.

TIP: Tap on QR code for connecting different device to Mobile hotspot via scanning QR code rather than entering in a password.

Configuring your mobile hotspot's settings

You can always modify your connection settings and security for your mobile hotspot.

1.   From your Settings, tap on Connections > then select Mobile hotspot & tethering > then Mobile hotspot.

2.   Tap on Configure for these settings:

- Network name: See and modify your wireless hotspot's name.

- Password: You may view or modify your security level which requires password.

- Band: Choose from among the several bandwidth choices.

- Security: Select mobile hotspot's security level.

- Advanced: Set up more hotspot settings.

Auto hotspot

When other devices are signed into the Samsung account of yours, your hotspot connection will be automatically shared with them.

1.   From your Settings, tap on 🛜 Connections > then on Mobile hotspot & tethering > then on Mobile hotspot.

2.   Tap on Auto hotspot, then you tap on 🌙 to turn on the feature.

Tethering

Employ tethering to share the device's connection to the internet with a different device. Service providers may offer several options.

1.   From your Settings, you should tap on 🛜 Connections > the select Mobile hotspot & tethering.

2.   Tap any option:

- You can tap on Bluetooth tethering, to help you share device's web connection via Bluetooth.

- You can connect your computer to any device with the use of USB cable, then you tap on USB tethering.

- Connect your computer to your device with the help of Ethernet adapter, then you should tap on Ethernet tethering.

Scanning for nearby device

Enabling Nearby devices scanning makes it simple to setup connections with other devices that are available. You'll receive a notification using this feature when devices are available for connection.

1.   From your Settings, you should tap on 📶 Connections > then select More connection settings > then select Nearby devices scanning.

2.   Tap on ⬇️ to enable the feature.

Ethernet

In the event that the connection to a wireless network is unavailable, you can link your mobile device with the local network using Ethernet cable.

1.   You should connect Ethernet cable to the device yours.

2.   From your Settings, tap on 📶 Connections > then select More connections settings > then Ethernet, then you follow the instructions.

190

TIP: An Ethernet cable cannot be connected to device without an adaptor, (which is not included).

The Networks lock status

See if your mobile device can be unlocked to use on a different mobile network by viewing its networks lock status. Options differ depending on the service provider.

❖ From your Settings, you should tap on Connections > then More connection-settings > then select Networks locks status.

Connected devices

You can attain a mobile continuity among connected devices, with yours and other devices.

❖ From your Settings, you should tap on Connected devices for these features:

- Quick Share: This permits the Sharing files to your device from anyone who uses their Samsung's account.

- Auto switches Buds: When you play media, make a call, or answer one, the Galaxy Buds will automatically transition from another gadget to this one.

- Calls and text on others devices: Let you answer and make calls as well as text messages with your Samsung devices which are signed to your own Samsung account.

- Continue applications on other devices: Lets you continue from where you had left off, with your Galaxy smartphone that have been signed to your own Samsung account.

- Links to Windows: To have immediate accessibility to the device's messages, images, and other content, you should connect it to a Windows pc.

- Multi controls: Use your Galaxy Book's keyboard and cursor. To operate this device & drag items back, & forth.

- Samsung's DeX: To improve multitasking, you should connect your mobile device to your TV or PC.

- Smart Views: Lets you Stream videos from any nearby TV or display the screen of your device.

- Galaxy Wearable: This let you Connect your Samsung earbuds and watch to your device.

- SmartThings: Connect your device into an ecosystem for smarter solutions for living.

- Android Auto: Helps Connect mobile device to compatible automobile display so you can concentrate on driving your car.

Sounds & vibrations

You can regulate the sounds & and vibrations for your screen touches, notifications, and other interactions.

Sound mode

Your sound mode can actually be change without the use of your volume keys of your device.

- ❖ From your Settings, you should tap Sounds & vibration, then you select a mode:

- Sound: you can apply the vibrations, sounds, and the volume levels that you have selected from your Sound settings as your alerts and notifications sound.

❖ Vibrates while ringing: Lets you set your smartphone to vibrate alongside your ringing tone whenever a call is received.

• Vibrate: This makes your device to vibrate only when you get alerts and notifications.

• Mute: This puts your device to total silence, making no sounds at all.

❖ Temporary mutes: Helps you set up limited time until your device gets muted.

TIP: You can utilize the settings of your sounds mode for changing your sound mode instead of your volume keys so won't lose your customized sound settings.

Mutes using gestures

You can easily mute your sounds, by turning your device over or simply by covering your screen.

❖ From your Settings, you should tap on Advanced features > then select Motions & gestures > then tap on Mute with gesture, then you tap on activate.

Vibrations

You can regulate when and how your mobile device vibrates.

1.   From your Settings, tap on 🔊 Sounds & vibration.

2.   Tap on any options to modify:

- Call vibrations: You can select from your preset vibration samples for your calls.

- Notifications vibrations: Let you select from your preset vibration models for your notifications.

- Systems vibration: You can setup your vibration intensity & feedback for these options below:

❖ System vibrations intensity: You should drag on your slider for adjustment of your vibration intensity.

❖ Touch interactions: Lets your device vibrates whenever you tap on your navigation buttons or you touch & hold any items on your screen.

- ❖ Dialing keypad: Makes your device screen vibrate whenever you dialing numbers from your Phone keypad.

- ❖ Samsung's keyboard: Makes device vibrate when are typing with your Samsung keyboard.

- ❖ Charging: Makes your device to vibrate once charger is plugged in.

- ❖ Navigation gestures: Makes it vibrate as you use the gestures.

- ❖ Camera's feedbacks: Vibrate when capturing photos, changing your shooting modes zooming, and many more.

- Vibrations intensity: Allows you setup the intensity level of your vibration for calls, touch interactions, and notifications via dragging on your sliders.

Volume

You can set the level of your volume for your call's ringtones, media, notifications, and your system sounds.

❖ From your Settings, you should tap on 🔊
Sounds & vibration > then Volume, then you
drag on your sliders for respective sound type.

TIP: To alter your volume, you may also utilize your
Volume keys. When pressed, your current sound type
and volume level are displayed in a pop-up's menu.
After expanding the menu with a tap, you may drag on
your sliders to adjust the loudness for your different
sound types.

Using your volume keys for the media

You can configure default action of your Volume keys
for regulating the volume of your media sound,
instead of whatever sound type that is being used.

1.   From your Settings, you should tap on 🔊
Sounds & vibration > then Volume.

2.   Tap on the Use Volume-keys for media for
activating this feature.

Your Media volume limits

You can limit your maximum volume output of your device's when using a headphone or Bluetooth speaker (not included).

1.   From your Settings, you should tap on Sounds & vibration > then Volume.

2.   Tap on More options > then select Media volume limits.

3.   Tap on to activate feature.

- To configure your maximum volume output, you should drag on your Custom's volume limits slider.

- To let a PIN modify your volume settings, you should tap on Set volume limits PIN.

Ringtones

You can add your own sounds or select from a selection of pre-made sounds for customizing your calls ringtones. Options differ depending on the service provider.

1.   From your Settings, you should tap on 🔊
Sounds & vibration > then Ringtone.

2.   Drag on your slider to regulate your ringtone's
volume.

3.   Tap on any ringtone to listen to a preview then
you choose it, or you tap on ⊥ Adds to use audio files
as your ringtone.

Notifications sound

You can select any set sound for all your notification
alerts.

1.   From your Settings, you should tap on 🔊
Sounds & vibration > then select Notification sound.

2.   Drag on your slider for the adjustment of your
notifications sound loudness.

3.   Tap on any sound to listen to a preview then
you select it.

 TIP: By utilizing your App's settings menu, you may
additionally customize your notifications sound,
making it peculiar for each of your app.

Notifications

You may streamline and prioritize application alerts through modifying which apps provide notifications & how you are alerted notification.

Application notifications

You can select apps you want to send notification.

❖ From your Settings, you should tap on Notifications > then App notifications, then you tap to turn on the notifications for each application.

Your Lock's screens notifications

You can select the notification you want on your Lock screen.

❖ From your Settings, tap on Notifications > then select Locks screens notifications, then you tap to activate the feature. Tap on an option for customization:

• Hiding content: Prevent notifications from appearing on your Notification panel.

• Show content: Help display notifications in your Notification panel.

- Shows contents while unlocked: Displays your notification contents whenever your screen is not locked.

- Notifications to shows: Select which notifications will be displayed on your Lock screen.

- Shows on Always On Displays: Help show notifications in your Always on Displays screen.

Pop-up style for notification

Your notifications' style and additional options are customizable.

- ❖ From your Settings, tap on Notifications > then select Notifications pop-up styles, then you select any pop-up style:

- Brief: This allows you to customize your notifications.

- ❖ Applications to show like brief: Select applications to display like a brief notification.

- ❖ Edges lighting styles: Helps select style of edges lightings for your notifications.

❖ Colors by keyword: Select personalized colors for the notifications that include keywords that are important to you.

❖ Shows even when screen is turned off: Select whether or not to display notifications even while your screen is off.

❖ Detailed: Turn on your default Notifications setting for your Samsung.

Do-not disturb

You can turn off notifications and audio when you're in the do-not disturb mode. It's also possible to designate exceptions for alarms, individuals, and apps. It is also possible to arrange regular activities such as meetings or sleep.

❖ From your Settings, tap on Notifications > then on Do-not disturbs then set up these:

• Do not disturb: To stop notifications & sounds, turn on "Do not disturb."

• For how much long? When you manually activate the Do Not Disturbs mode, you can select your default duration.

Schedule

- Sleeping: Create a personalized sleep routine for the "Do not disturb" mode.

- Add a schedule: Make a new routine to set up the days and hours to consistently place your mobile device on do not-disturb mode.

Permitted during Do-not disturb

- Calls & messages: Tap on to grant Do-not disturb exceptions.

- Application notifications: Add the applications from which you want to get notifications when in "Do-Not Disturb" mode. Even if you deny the associated applications access, you will still receive call, message, and chat notifications.

- Alarms & sounds: While your "Do not disturb" is active, you can turn on sounds & vibrations for events, reminders, and alarms.

- Hide notifications: To hide your notifications, check the customization options.

Notifications Advanced settings

You can set up your notifications from your applications & services.

- ❖ From your Settings, tap on 📷 Notifications > then Advanced settings.

- Shows notification icons: Adjust the number of notifications that show up in your Status bar.

- Shows battery percentages: The Status bar will show you how much battery life your smartphone currently has.

- Notification history: Show last few & snoozed notifications.

- Conversations: View notifications related to conversations. To make a conversation notification priority, alert, or mute, touch & hold it.

- Floating notifications: Select to activate the floating notifications, between the Smart pop-ups' views or Bubbles.

- Suggest actions & replies to notifications: Receive relevant suggestions for operations to notifications and responds to messages.

- Show snooze button:

- Showing snooze button: Allow a button to be displayed so you may swiftly snooze notifications.

- Notifications reminders: Activate and personalize recurring reminders concerning notifications from certain applications and services. To switch off the reminders, clear your notifications.

- Application icon badges: Determine which applications possess active notifications having badges which show up in their icons. Tap to select whether your badges show the amount of your unread notifications.

- Wireless Emergencies Alerts: Personalize emergency alert notifications to your preferences.

Alert when you pick up phone

You can configure your smartphone to vibrate once you take it up to notify you of missed messages and calls.

❖ From your Settings, you should tap on Advanced features > then select Motions & gestures > then Alerts when phone is picked up to activate.

Display

You may set up your screen's brightness, font sizes, timeouts delay and many more display settings of your choice.

Dark mode

The Dark mode lets you change to much darker theme so as to help your eyes to be more relaxed at night times, bright screens, darkening white and notifications.

❖ From your Settings, tap on Display for these options:

• Light: Helps apply light colors themes to the device (by default).

- Dark: Helps apply dark colors themes to the device.

- Dark modes settings: Lets you customize where & when your Dark mode will be applied.

❖ Turns on as it scheduled: Setups your Dark mode to be between the Sunset-sunrise/Custom schedule.

Your Screen brightness

Regulate your screen brightness as to your personal preference or your lighting surroundings.

1.   From your Settings, you should tap on Display.

2.   Customize settings under Brightness:

- Drag on your Brightness slider for setting up your personal brightness level.

- Tap on the Adaptive brightness on your screen to help you automatically adjust the brightness of your screen, that is based on your lighting conditions.

❖ If your Adaptive brightness has been disabled, you can tap on Extra brightness for increasing your maximum brightness level. This consumes more battery.

 TIP: You can decide to adjust your screen brightness using your Quicks settings pane.

Motions smoothness

Increasing the refresh rate of your screen will result in realistic-looking animations and smoother scrolling.

1.   From your Settings, tap on   Display > then select Motion smoothness.

2.   Tap any option, then you tap on Apply.

Eyes comfort shield

This feature could lessen eye strain and improve your quality of sleep. This feature can be scheduled to turn on and off automatically.

1.   From your Settings, tap on   Display > then select Eyes comforts shield, then you tap on   to activate this feature.

2.   You can tap on any of these options for customizing:

Adaptive, helps you regulates the color temperature of your screen based on time of the day and your usage trends.

❖ Customize your schedule to determine when to activate the Eyes Comforts Shield.

❖ Tap on Set schedule then you select Always on, custom or Sunset to sunrises.

❖ Drag on your Color temperature's skidder to set up the opacity of your filter.

• Enhanced your comfort to help you adjust your contrast and color tones of your display for a much comfortable viewing.

Screen mode

There are multiple screen mode selections on your device that let you modify your screen quality under various scenarios. The mode can be changed to suit your preferences.

1.   From your Settings, tap Display > then select Screen mode.

2.   Tap on any option to setup a distinct screen mode.

- Drag your slider for adjusting your white balance.

- Tap on Advanced settings for manual change of your RGB values.

Lifting to wake

You can turn on your screen just by lifting your mobile device.

❖ From your Settings, you should tap on Advanced features > then select Motions & gestures > and then Lifts to wakes for enabling this feature.

Double tapping for turning on screen

Instead of you using your Side key, you can turn your screen on by double-tapping.

❖ From your Settings, tap on Advanced features > then select Motions & gestures > then Double taps to turn-on screens to activate this feature.

Double tapping for turning off screen

Instead of you using your Side key, you can turn your screen off by double-tapping.

❖ From your Settings, tap on Advanced features > then select Motions & gestures > then Double taps to turn off screens to activate this feature.

Keeping your screen on when viewing

To keep your screen turned on, by employing your front camera for detecting whenever you're looking your screen.

❖ From your Settings, tap on Advanced features > then select Motions & gestures > then on Keep screens on while viewings, then you tap on to activate the feature.

The One-handed mode

The layout of your screen can be adjusted, so that it accommodates using your mobile device via one hand.

1.   From your Settings, tap on ⚙ Advanced features > then select One-handed mode.

2.   Tap on 🌙 to activate the feature then you choose any of these options:

- Gesture: You should Swipe downward at center of your screen bottom edge.

- Button: Tap on ⬜ Home double times quickly to reduce size of your display.

Lock screens & security

By enabling a screen lock, you may protect your information and secure your smartphone.

Types of Screen lock

Your screen lock types that give medium, high, or no security are as follows: None, PIN, Pattern, Swipe, and Password.

Note: It is also possible to secure sensitive data in your smartphone and prevent unauthorized access using your biometric locks.

Setting up your secure screen's locks

This is very compulsory to set up and activate biometric locks. You have to secure your device using a secure screen lock (Pattern, PIN, or Password).

1. From your Settings, tap on 🔒 Lock screen > then select Screens locks types then you tap on a secured screen lock (PIN, Pattern or Password).

2. Tap on ⬇ to turn on showing notifications in your lock screen. These are the available options:

    - Hide contents: This helps conceals your notifications in your Notification panel.

    - Show content: Help display notifications in your Notification panel.

    - Shows contents when unlocked: Display notification contents if your screen is not locked.

    - Notifications to shows: Help select what notifications should display on your Lock screen.

1. Tap on Done, then exit your menu.

2. Set up these options of screen locks:

- Smart Lock: This feature unlocks your mobile device automatically once it detects other devices or trusted locations. This feature requires secured screens lock.

- Secured locks settings: Modify the settings for your secured lock. This feature requires secured screens lock.

- Lock screen: You should Touch to modify the appearance and items on your lock screen.

- Widgets: On your Lock screen, tap to modify your widgets that show up next to the clock.

- Touch & hold for edit: Select whether to enable touch & hold editing of items on your Lock screen.

- Always On Displays: This activates your Always On Displays screen.

- Roaming clock: When you're roaming, this display the time at home and wherever you are.

- About lock screen: Update the software on your lock screen.

❖ From your Settings, you should tap on Google, then you choose an option for customization.

Date & time

By default, your wireless network provides time and date information to your device. You can manually set your time & date even when you are within a network coverage.

❖ From your Settings, you should tap on General management > then select Date & time. These are the available options:

• Automatic date & time: This obtains time & date updates from wireless network. If your Automatic date & time is deactivated, these are the available options:

❖ Set date: Lets you type in your current date.

❖ Set time: Allows you enter your current time.

• Automatic time zones: This utilizes time zones given by your device network.

❖ Select times zones: Let you select new time zones.

- Setup time zones based on locations: Obtains time updates which are based on location.

- Use 24-hour formats: Helps select the format by which you display your time.

Customization service

Your Samsung devices, applications, & services are developed to offer you customized services through clever and intelligent prediction of your wants and desires. Based on the data that Samsung collects about you and how you use its services, Samsung's Customization Service offers recommendations and customized content to improve your overall experience.

❖ From your Settings, you should tap on General management > then select Customization service.

Troubleshooting

You may look for software upgrades and also reset your device's services when needed.

Software update and System updates

You can always search for available updates on software and then you can install on your device. Service providers may offer several options.

❖ From your Settings, you should tap on System update/Software updates for these options:

- Checks for updates: This helps you manually look for updates on software.

- Checks for software updates: Let you manually search for updates for software.

- Continue update: Helps you resume updates which was interrupted.

- Shows software updates history: Help you see the list of every software update in your device.

- Smart updates: Helps you automatically install security updates.

- Uses software upgrade assistants: Helps install tool for installing system updates.

Reset

Reset your devices & your network settings. Additionally, you may reset device to the factory defaults.

Resetting all settings

All of the settings on your device are reset to their factory defaults, with the exception of your security, account settings and language. Private information is unaffected.

1.   From your Settings, tap on General management > then select Reset > then Reset-all settings.

2.   Tap on the Reset settings, then you confirm once prompted.

Resets networks settings

The Resets networks settings allows you to reset Bluetooth, mobile data, and Wi-Fi settings.

1.   From your Settings, tap on General management > the select Reset > then Resets networks setting.

2.   Tap on Reset settings, then you confirm once prompted.

Resetting accessibility settings

Resetting your device accessibility settings can be done. The Accessibility settings from your downloaded applications and from your own data will not be affected.

1.   From your Settings, then tap on ⚏ General management > then select Reset > then Resets the accessibility settings.

2.   Tap on Reset settings, then you confirm once prompted to.

Reset Factory Data

It is possible to erase all data on your smartphone by resetting it to its factory settings.

All of the device's data, including downloaded applications, application data & settings, system, Google or additional account settings, music, pictures, videos, with other files, are permanently deleted with this action. There is no impact on any data kept in an additional SD card.

Your Google Devices Protections is turned on automatically when you configure your lock screen while signed into your Google account in your device.

Note: It may require a full day for a Google Account's password reset to take effect across all your account's linked devices.

Before you reset your device

1.   You should confirm that the details you wish to retain has transferred into the storage area.

2.   Verify your password & user name by logging into your account with Google.

For resetting your device do these

1.   From your Settings, you should tap on General management > then Reset > then Factory data resets.

2.   Tap on Reset, then follow the direction to perform your reset.

3.   For setting your device, follow the instructions when it restarts.

Your Google Devices Protection

Your Google Devices Protection is activated once you sign into any Google Account in your mobile device and set up Lock screen. Through the use of your Google account details to confirm your identity, this service guards against unwanted factory data reset on your phone.

Enabling your Google Devices Protection

Your Google Devices Protection is activated automatically when you set a lock screen and add Google Account on your device.

Disabling your Google Devices Protection

You may either delete your lock screen or remove every Google Accounts from your device to turn off Google Devices Protection.

If you want to remove your Google accounts do these

1.   From your Settings, tap on Accounts & backup > then select Manage accounts > then [Google Account].

2.   Tap on Remove account.

For removing secure Locks screen do these

1.   Go to your Settings, then you should tap on 🔒 Lock screen > then select Screen locks type.

2.   Tap on either the Swipe/None.

Made in the USA
Monee, IL
06 July 2024

61357686R00122